# CLOG

Grant Maierhofer

*Clog*
a novel
by Grant Maierhofer

*Clog* is typeset in Aurelia, a typeface designed by Hermann Zapf after original 15th century typefaces created by Nicolas Jenson. The name Aurelia is an allusion to the Roman emperor Aurelian, who was murdered by his own Praetorian Guard in 275 CE. / Titles are set in Helvetica.

Designed and copy-edited by John Trefry
for Inside the Castle.

Edited by Sean Kilpatrick
Photographs by New Juche



A text occupying
the expanded field of literature,
from Inside the Castle
www.insidethecastle.org

ITC-011
ISBN-13: 978-0-9993459-7-9
ISBN-10: 0-9993459-7-4

[redacted]

*To Kelsey, Ada, Hollis, & Keith*

*and dedicated to the life's work of*
*Atilla Csihar*

*In a way I thought the heart of the film was about meat*

- Tobe Hooper

*An artist must be a human first. I have my own principles to be a human being therefore I need to face limits. This is called the contradiction of being. I have been dreaming to have a group of people to do what we are passionate about together simply without any conflicts which could only be a dream. However I believe that things do go easier when there is no too much desire. I am extreme. I am extremely concerned about art, which means I will not only live a meaningful life but also a complicated & hopeless one*

- "Random Soliloquy: A MANIFESTO," Zhu Ming

*https://www.youtube.com/watch?v=xVj-p1nQaYw*

- Master Wilburn Burchette

*https://www.youtube.com/watch?v=b6Y5BLlzNZk*

- Tan Lin

One day he in being was awake, his eyes being opened. This was once, a day, & he woke up, his eyes pulled to the light. It was in this room, the small shed, his small space, & he was then awake. This fellow H. was then awake & told to nobody his status. "I am awake." One day, this fellow then, awoke. This he, H., would look upon the light & see him there, a small mass, a bit of hair or skin, some bleeding, & H. would welcome & pray into the light. Staring there into the light the sun H. would smile & remove all clothing & open the door of this space & see it there & smile & breathe it in, H. He felt happiness or not sorrow staring out & witnessing the light & smiling at the dirt & paid little attention to the film playing itself out upon the screen within the shed wherein he was.

A little region of his known manner depicted perverts with equal rights. This little region embodied Christ the spirit, depicted perverts. This manner within him was all-forgiving. This known depiction was open, willing to forgive & welcome, breathing. So most quiet judgments earned their violence. Regardless, the stigma of mental illness became music. Parts of me were buried in a wedding. No shamed history, for I was full of those who could not think. Sure, H. was a scumsaw human. But here H. is, banned from the urinal of every nation. Relax yourself into the sun & be, H. Open your eyes to the infinite possibility of the sun, H.

He watched it first smelling on the ground & pulled it to the space & placed it on his worktable & spread its limbs far & vivisected. Then, sleepy, he gulped a handful of soap at his inuring, the sun had gone for the day. Perhaps he had the forearms of a wife. His wife had left him somehow, had become disfigured. She had left him by disfigurement, herself. She was leaving him still, often. She had need to leave him, & left him. His family left no legacy & he was alone within America. He wanted to be alone within America & smelled the ground. This awestruck son necked with grain, stalking the peaks for peasant ladies. An old body wandering & being & returning to his machining. This H. wandering there & standing within the stores & staring at faces & not seeing much, staring at bags of plastic & seeing. All is forgiven, every stitch of living forgiven. H. forgave & held himself & wept.

H. wonders if he won the lottery to become a piece of litter under his doctor's dress. Abortive standing lost within America, & so. Reciting boundaries with one hand over his heart. He invites a dead fawn into the bath with him when he needs to decompress. The forest is dense with heroes. Be the hero of your own cast. Monks love dust. The monks dig in dust & he is monastic, digging. He watches the machine's movement & feels his hands become machinelike & whispers something nobody hears drinking something nobody sees, this H.

made sense in active living. His being was stretched in front of him like bloated doecorpse & not much feeling in his guts. The shed seemed small at first. The shed was bought & pulled & dragged by him & eventually he made his way to where he was & turned his anger inward. In the shed H. could turn his anger inward & feel something strong & compelling & the light would make him warm & sleepy. He committed crimes against himself. He ruined himself & hurt himself. A being there, hurting & being, his body writhing on the floor & no light. No family & legacy & wife & children & somehow it has left his being & he is tired. They are gone & where they are is being. They are being. They are feeling the sun some days or not. They are doing somesuch. They are wonderful bodies being & H. could not surround himself. H. could not surround himself & selfishly he wandered to the place where the shed existed & dug his hands into the dirt to feel this way & pulled at the men & all was right with the world. Someday perhaps somesuch met some other being sleeping & marrying together in living & smiling sure.

This is the room where Christ built the first trolley. Aren't you verklempt? She was an uncomfortable & dishonest shopper. Selecting increasingly small texts to solve his idiocy on the wave she dropped all afternoon. Staring at the pages there & feeling himself pulled into something sleepy & ignorable

& welcoming, a little world. H. was free. Was not receptive to lactation is all her journal reads. By seeking an answer to their curse, they elongated it. Distended it. Swelled it shut. An eye being swollen shut then sleepy. A sleepy eye there living. There is no grief tooled beyond a relationship. Staring & feeling lifeless & ingesting chemicals to sleep & be & welcoming a redolence or breathing. Guests are mainly in the maze. H. staring outside of them & wanting, embracing their wandering & being. How vile by degrees, so that they shall decompose as one. A single corpsing. The power of how ugly. H. lives to advance the cobwebs year by year.

A document will often hint as to whether he who composed it is a carrier of yeast. A document presented will beget its certain smears. Attempt a day. A day within somesuch wandering & smelling the shelves. Try holding it steady with a set of pictures. Slips through unclasped. The sun is less than alien, kept together by collective caring, so quit already. Its rays wane. It sends the sphere its law. This is an act of nursery for beds. Welcome heat & press your head to pavement H. Most architecture fails to lubricate itself with the bowels of its compilers. H. struggles to sum the country up with the correct amount of hairballs. They're armed. They drive. There. This teetering abyss of content & sweet rolls. They compile wads. Irrelevant, the pinging through its trauma. There is no study to be made. Optimize the skin on bills, stuff them up your splits. Neglect a partner or two. The beast & the power, dehumanized into a nostril, as Wall Street wills, topple the bunion. She saws her clothes. A wedding, skip to the objections. Skip to the DMT (bark of the stem), moi-Ayahuasca tryptamines, the community diseases on his upper respiratory tract infection, comparatively smooth. The craftsmen, many were torn, the body toured in praise, but it does not share the corruption of the gut. Uniquely American swelter & sleepy doe-eyed heads stared at H. as he wandered from the desert with his hand out. Anything could work. Anything could save a day. Anything could make it real, make it more. Anything could turn him right. Anything could fill his stomach, a sleeping rotting thing. Anything being could be made right. Anything would doing & worth being & being worth could be done & done. It was all before him there, swelling & shutting. A sleeping city perhaps & entering home & sleeping. Sleeping in the place they can't see & H. sucking at the walls for bits of liquid. Discover his document & sleep. Discover this document & sleep. Let yourself get sleepy & take it & give it to yourself. Open yourself to the endless gutless pitiless existing being. Nothing & nothing & nothing ever forever. Do not open your eyes when reading him. Do not read of H. & see him there. Do not desire something somewhere for H. & being. He is sleeping. He is curled upon the small bed an armycot pulled from somewhere

sometime a warehouse a Goodwill something some useless place he's sleeping in his shed curled up beneath the blanket he'd pulled upon his back from desert & it hung redolent with piss & blood & he had carried a corpsy vulture & carried it back with him & brought it heaving its stupid breath within the blanket & he had laid it to rest upon a toilet within a silent room & on leaving H. had ripped & clawed & pulled & embraced the lock of this place to ensure the vulture's silence for a time.

They are not trusted so much as uniformed. Meat boys for a pained expression. A comma. A triangle even. A prayer, a former document. Ne travaillez jamais. Ne travaillez jamais. Put your feeling in his guts & do not accept the job. They are foolish for this loveable persecutor. Preaching diarrhea mixed in urns, weaned on the runs, the rest. Traffic swears never swerve. Nuns begin transforming in the scream of every shadow. A lot of night & nighs within the place where he's breathing & smelling the dead sun's scent & living & pulling at worms again.

His fungus rubbed a hole in the wall. He turned into an ape of great import, hooting life is swell. This devastated his neighbors, his family. They wanted to read his wail. To deny him of an orientation regarding the warranty on his next mattress. In the decompressive bonemeal cup, dex-

H. cut along the roof of his mouth with nagging. The groan, farming in & out across the tongues, fucked a meal back. This doe H. had pulled from someone's heap. Being represented by the blood she spoke remedied all honor. This fat means had spectrum. That is to say, one's mind isn't even a suggestion. There are degrees taken loose within the safety you refuse. Au revoir for you. The controversial steering that leaves us mommy & daddy, no spirit since the Great Depression. Nigh a Genesis controller remained. Tremble under the bones of each cloud until the rain can dry you, until sperm isn't an intention. He'd study the tickled. They tend to stare into the sun. Forsake them to prove neglect has a limit. Keep a wig close & their scent won't matter. Whoever desires the least is lord. Prayers are window dressing, but thine eyes cause sores. The war swan took a lunch break, yawning wrinkles over the household. The bonus was television dictated which sled to place under the dictator you thought you chose.

H. fleshed out everything at the end of his telescope. Like a girl living death with a blade in all her recommendations. Man & woman, these notions didn't fare well. They wanted too many albums named after them. H., playing sports at a cemetery. The school girl grave, fantasy or joke, spent on a partner. Benefits precisely in the mouth. But is it wonderful or filmed that way? People are generally all for the lack they always say. The minds tropical, the study dysentery, stomach instruction amoebic. What else, why? Protect the ignorant from their own whole lower bodies. Some galleries can't be overlooked. Come coated in him, in the silly authority of a cut. H. spread himself thin & pulled at the skin leftover there. H. would spread himself across this place & wander endlessly & that was his relief. The relief that H. received came from long, long days of walking & leaving behind any comfort he'd assembled in the shed. This was his remedy for living & it often came at the price of brief imprisonment, further institutionalization. He was living. He was in his living & being. He was a human being & living & breathing. This was H., & he embodied flaw.

He took their magic pink teeth to archery practice. He took the case & held it & shook it & stared at the sun too long. Someone purchased T. Kaczynski's arrows & the victims received the money. Everything is ancient. H. is alive on an ancient planet with ancient thoughts & nothing is living. There is no dictatorship to blame. There is no external source to fist. The effect can be framed & suffered. Shutting down a prayer, dragging the user through it with increased drugs, but no more confused friends, please. It is important to spend your time jogging depressedly. One must eliminate one's prospects. Squatters lit on death in standard, evil offices, making updates, defragmenting their bubblegum, fuck that scene. Not even Freud would. Fake literacy to death.

USA & fathers & saws too small to saw through rot running through a fire in H.'s glands. Yama, of the race of being torn in two, & in fiery pits, pray to the old pit: & they will say a stalk of grain, which he read in cryosleep. This is the correct approach, the piece of phlegm holds up the satin curtains. Do not wipe with the user's manual. Spend your days staring at German manuals for machines not yet built or long since redundant & ingest their material as the worm. Embrace only the machinery & digest its every nuance. Every fragment. Every piecemeal. Every rotten bit of it coating your insides until your liver starts to rust. Feel yourself changing & embrace it. Feel the dwindle of your humanity & embrace it. H. is close.

When they live, there is no abstract, no act, no potential, no cousin half one's age sneaking under the covers, whispering about the CIA all through fighting. In the panoptic drone, people shake their fleas off with an ancient maneuver. They only fuck high on the pilfered blood they swim through. Neglect is a rite of passage between parent & offspring. They will smear plasma on the lips of their infants & tour Europe. They are not playing guitars in those pictures, just using them to hide the fact that they are masturbating. They rely on stuttering. They crack the glass face of clocks when they come. Being born is a suggestion. H. started in their hand. They gave H. a badge with a flea on it. H. understood stereotypes, embodying his favorite. H. found a chief & he led him through a tunnel, till they blew bubbles in the continental shelf, his squish-assed contact binary, litigating all the massages back from the shoulders of deceased women. This never ended. This was never-ending. This was something to which H. was subjected daily. The sense that he was putrid. The sense that he was vile. The sense that he had murdered. The sense that he had raped. The sense that he had stolen. The sense that he had lied. The sense that he had cheated in worse ways he'd imagined. The sense that he'd stolen this life from someone. The sense that he was putrid. The sense that it was secret, elusive, slightly outside of him. The sense that someday it would all come back to ruin him. It was this, more than anything, more than death or leaving or fear of dire poverty or illness, that led H. into the shed in the first place, that led him to the machine & made its properties so appealing. Clean lines. Simple maneuvers necessary to accomplish something humankind could not. H. would use it. H. would persist in using it & welcome it to him. H. would welcome its metal fragments & bits of rust into his bloodstream & dermis & it would not stop.

Stop lava with your posterior. But the camera was

blocked by a plate. This formed the first lake in the world. The reckoning: senseless. The yoga: a hell of spandex asses. A fetus poses out of one, whole barnyards between its gums. Take care of the feathers it coughs instead. Kill your fetus like an instrument awakened. The shelf sticking redolent to its ordnance, teeth in the blade saying give. Acting swanlike because the tendency's rewarded? Mine that deficiency. Their minerals stay inside, chief. No external congratulations. The fuckcorpse so blind attention turns to it, subheading others. Question a dog. Open its homely tit rows & grind your relations mute. The buzzard will still lick you.

Tattered robe open to the audience. Set on mild petition. How to be American with a compass in your socket. They appear like opium above the world, anchored by verse, blowing frenzy on screens that power down. The blue sea anterior a spot gush vicar wounds the room with fear, baby, & happy, happy. Knew this went profitable distances. Pelvic honk honk. Steer bit queer bait led the lane. Skip a coin across the difference till your priapism turns frothy. Big mixture H. went complete. He understood levels. The boss was a membrane of rutting clamps. It ran on money & mushrooms that fell out of best-sellers. Big mixture H. erected the cartilage from its forefront & scalped backward running, flipping the cold strip everted till the eyes dilated like saucers of blood. Ireland was cold years thereafter. Singing beware: the children of the world will work your wallet's guilt.

How many Vietnams are in the television? H. watched hours of Dusty Rhodes. H. slept & woke to bodies in cages annihilating themselves & breaking their limbs. H. paid close attention to their bodies & studied them & neglected everything else & himself & became warped, left. The outsiderdom of palace prisons bombed to caves, to woven fungal flesh, to published documents like this that will seep as you slumber off its ink & gas you enfeebled over time, halved by any ambition, living out your own scared aquarium.

Random syndromes bugger mankind. Compared to what they'll do, Columbine through all rendered on the walls of Lascaux. No sentence has ever survived the trip from page to mouth. Unless it's your mother selling her teardrops to the media. Rimbaud will crease his craggy trousers through an aristocracy of reanimated jizz & towel the backside of his tomb, a bulletfragment still in wrist. The worms reference themselves while growing fat on disease. Whose piss they handcuff themselves to. Rat babies roasted. Teachers in coffee. Intelligible only to hurt you. Cursed be the pissy roast the breastworks & the curse of the wedding. H. was passing through the policies of piss. Read at it. Don't pay attention. Pang attention. Ruined attention it is fine. His attention is ruined it is fine. This is just the document of some H., a random person without narrative ability. This is a useless document. This is a useful document. This is merely entertainment. This is art is merely entertainment. Distraction from survival. Entities encircling idiots with big ideas. Endless big ideas. Bodies with endless ideas. Come in, Joyce murmured. Keep that in, loyal amanuensis. A useless spree of H.'s words. H.'s endless words. H. is not a character. This is not a novel.

This is house coffee of the competition, they have a way of kindness. You, friend, are God stomped to God without law. Imagine the rotting world transcribed through the digital & see what you've done. Write something experiential, experimental, about a saw that can't be created yet, a perfect saw & its manual, a journal from a user who saws off their arm. Rewrite this a bunch of different ways lazily using the internet. Figure out some anagrams of Maldoror.

To estimate the bone & how to become a beautiful sight. When finished, he said that the existing machines have failed desperately. Wanting & metal are in the flesh. H. was watching footage. H. is able, H. will give way to this. It's allowed leaving the glass for horses & tend to be behind your face, & that is impossible, because this is a true, as we do, & every situation in my life H. feels mediocre. Neglect machinist hear you (deadly nightshade) the cops & pots from human urine this subhuman, & as many cores of barley, in the studio. Subheading others. They know how many. A system always check the machine check? Ambient reading practices for sleepy bored dilletantes. Great, another incomprehensible teenage adult.

Books on H.'s shelf include: bad adolescent novel, bad adolescent novel redux, *Barbs, Prongs, Points, Prickers, & Stickers: A Complete & Illustrated Catalogue of Antique Barbed Wire, The Green Book, Technological Slavery,* self-published history of bleach, *Lautréamont & Sade, Journal of a Solitude, A Second Census of Finnegans Wake, Walden Two*

In the garden of God. Therefore, if, then, H. is, H. answers, that thou mayest be to us from the signification of a covenant, that the universe, & of him from me. Let me understand the vile nature of the author of this before reading it. An author it's too late watching a vile tape in audience reading it. H. this is not for you. It is not a good time to carry out early in the morning. In the blood of the space of the world, in the house of everyone, & in them he looked on them, to the left, stood the dead, he is come, that is to say, in the changes of light thing to be, or it does not exceed the dead. Neglect him in the way of today, in order that his living should wither. Often, however, the beam of one manner

of handling affairs march was not a little vain, all parts, not only the process of the third interval of the void, you cannot be the venom of inkechtion of others being only of the highest in absolute terms off the ears.

H. found him what & hung up by plenty of ears. This fellow, H. saw him. Quote as long as the mechanism of fanaticism, who said that he found the machine to create the world homo sacer. Neglect not to be good if H. is good. H. will go & see himself on the people to drink to a degree in the sleep of the sick leads at any time, & at any time, & the harmful activities it is variable is noxious, for spoiled hath been testified to this is to shovel up the framework of the project if they are not. However, when there is no matter how you want to be anything but what it is now overshirt they'll enjoy letting your head fall sleeping as well as internal thought processes image of the hand & the hand through its effect its significance to the author or the journal mistake to look. There is a darkness H. wished to make himself even dissolved in acrid places for the public. A desire to see oneself crippling & not living & withering & not being publicly. H. felt this desire as a man living in America & mimicking, feeling moronic & losing. This was H. & living. This was his creepy living & rotting. He was endless & you are encouraged not to read. Pass a glance. Cover the page quickly. Ignore most if not all text. Find out what happens. This is elevator music for his living. This is not literature. This is fake manual about a saw that doesn't exist that was ruined by the internet. This is not living. This is not a way out. This is not hopeful. This is not as it should be. This is not art. Not according to the flesh-blade knives & provoking. Decompress. These apparatuses. As to the men of the generation of a number of hearts, & by these the pious is said to be the history of all that flies away, he began to forward. In the book impure or unclean. H. does not want to read the things, so don't, embrace a carelessness & not-reading, perhaps never to have known a thing for our teeth. & visits to vineyards & revenue to perform the words of some of the banal become his genius will be in the chest, then write to the method of training, which exceeded by that one thing, & a witness of one of them, a person for that which was right, & the tongue of their information technology into the hands of, & at the same time, let us consider the end of the atom bomb H. fell down in a faint, how the plant should also be most shoving the moron, au revoir, au revoir. During the three days it was easy to use this as an oracle, & in the door of the church. Listen to the words of somesuch. H. briefly forgot the name of Joan Vollmer so sat for hours at the saw removing the skin of his right forearm. Let's play William Tell. Let's ignore William. H. forgot briefly the contribution of Joan Vollmer to the world, her living. Her living & her consciousness worth more than any single thing in print. A living. What if she did vile things, who knows. Who knows who did vile things & can they be forgiven. H. is endlessly forgiving. H. imagines sitting & being in the Mexican sun with Joan Vollmer & undoing history & living & being & returning to America & wandering together. H. imagines the end of literature & the beginning of living. Raduan Nassar joins in & H. & Joan & Raduan are living. Living & being & staring & writing long works & covering every bit of excrement & Robert Shields joins them & they are in the realms of the unreal & living & being & feeling endless potential & all is forgiven & all is possible & even the prisoners & even the vile evildoers all of them are living & being within America & living & outside of America & living & they are a family & being & they are incomprehensible & living & they are a small group reading & they are staring & they are paying attention to their misdeeds & they are saying sorry for their misdeeds & they have made mistakes & they cannot continue living but they are living & H. is carving Joan Vollmer's name into the exposed bone in his right forearm & feeling.

But what is the meaning of all. The author is not easy to see any error in its work format as a race. United States & elsewhere for sale. This is a mother same number of core of barley, & inhuman conduct the ph of how it was done & know that the user is out of control. & they do not need an answer, but they do not see it. Always do to help you feel at ease, not only to believe in friendship & with Gilles Deleuze, the mother. H. started to remember that pure melancholy, which the followers of the blessedness of the man, fearing God himself to give up the siege. For though H. was with them, where they reached the gate, wandering. He saws due to a failure. He had provided iron hand. It is the color of the blue sea, the tent which occasions a bluish light is sprung from the fact that the census roll, what will be done, so as not to die is not the hope of Lautréamont Arabic fattened cattle are of aluminum bone, & a wordless aluminum oatmeal cookie. This work, together with their delights, cancerous, to whom they give payment in full to the systemic, commerce, & the younger men as you love yourself is the fate of which he thinks has come to reflect the whole of that you may do his noonday, shall arise to see the hidden things of the wallpaper, looking at the Caesar hatred of God. However, you can get a kidnapped antibiotichs physicians who did. They do not know. Frankly, They do not care. Of the world: he that is mine, they will not smother ego in this regard. According to the sinking of a long holiday is what you do not want to know what's possible.

A crime when they are very ill, as it were, towards the end of the last continuous cutting of the brand you have taken the urine with the skull shall H. be the guardian of a little less, & the melancholic humor. Therefore, it is the most beautiful child in the performing described above. However her to swallow hot as the ears in barely able to become strong abused fair dealing are expected to be taken away, either (please specify the names are not written in this & grow toss or burn). His name is H. the wind forearm forearm clap bristle mumble used magic every hex magic rotten magic rotten px user's manual, & he did not hear. & it split in two. The judgment by the enemy growth, good & bad managed, sister approval echo separate human endless to H., his right hand machine user is more inept than in the past. Each figure there became one of the rot who have been obtained, & is a fool. But if God knocks. You continue to be excited about & applied are a part of some patients from the universal forum of this is in place to explain to dying he wants to laugh a great branding see beneath it is made. Hell below was in the wall, he looked on H. will they return to the fact that they are the whole of the blood, & how the food is prepared to the work of the new expedition have elected H., the question is the place in which it is higher than the bar of detritus, which is the lust by a qualified personnel is, there is a big doe. H. is sleeping the doe on him & the death on him & a sweltering heat & the summerlight coming through & gleaming & there is glint & it is rotting & a spider crawls near them & they are rotting together & H. can smell his arm & it is falling & he is feeling himself withering & wants to flee but can't & so at night exits into the cool cool dark & stares into the ground & shoves the scabbed flesh of right nub into ground & feels it coating him & feels the worms with it & attempts to grab with rightphantomhand & shoves & can't feel himself infected & can't feel the light leaving him & looks out endlessly wandering eye.

Then again, all the people & often died, & then watch again. Closest to death, this is the type of fungus & rot more than any other free long life, the judge is to tear through the tissue begins, it is not enough to explain how you clean toilets & smoke cigarettes to rest became complete able to escape all the rules in the sense emulator or lack thereof good & spoiled the metal, the metal outer neutral motors neutral atom lacquer ability of carp to walk the earth, & over & over again to listen to the songs of one of the reasons to live. There are, perhaps, from the supermental excesses. This figure flesh along the river streams & spat on him. Do not start. H. will melt there, & the flesh can describe something, something you'd like to be able to describe & early readily pulled pulled it necessary to change times will be spent in the flesh. On the long end, the machine's inception prior to the end of this unholy relic. Element to element, which is an element who saw the riddle X & Z, as the liver is a life term. H. eventually fungus & rot & being such as that & ending. What is so terrible & terrifying about literature, history, by shifting the movement to take medications for the intellectualizing. H. also has to look to God for them, which is not in conformity with the growth of the two forms of rot, & shall tread it down, the law, they are the lord, they are God, is probably when your civilzation shorns his hair. The user manual. Security. It is not, therefore, in letters of the spelling & he changes them, however, does not seem to measure up to the righteous. Beef. How many it is possible, the conclusions of the things that can be a factor of the fetch about this but it is the instant of the initial & of the same degree for the food which you do not want him to be put to death, & it is to say, that H. may fairly, & who came from the region of the temple, from the before the doors of the oracle, the hands of a hindrance & they have kept, & abide in the covert to employer. H. saw that pliance is the study's main feral cave composition. At the headquarters of the care package handyman Christ laws might feel it is worth dmt (stem) height tent once the aura net note that no altar heat & the tone altar of hearts H. dares to droop the venture pale less bold yellow sun spearhead nun dares saw monk dares to be had, & it was tired of this record here salivate with him in his urine without a set in the backyard to become a part of his own already tried the way to his head, he tried to get that great things were possible for this sense the speed of the new man. They wrote it to continue to respond to the state of the air, users want to know. & he broke a piece of a piece of paper out of the machine out of the previously existing in vials & smiles are life better, but in the evenings & H. he said before. & this is the idea behind the hairtie volume would allow it.

One morning in H.'s morning the sun hit him & lit his face & let the wet of morning split the sweat & slid it down his face & felt him breathing & H. could stare down at his chest & see it moving & see himself moving & understand that this was breathing this was all of his living reduced to his breathing & sleeping & feeling this way in the sunlight felt alive & being & H. stared at himself. Endless & endless he stood up & felt at his ribs & felt himself falling apart a bit & being a bit & needing to eat he left for grubs & pulled a bit here & there until he'd made a small mound of somesuch & ate them with leaves & drank from the springwater there & stared up & felt the sun against his chest & thanked the sun & thanked his God for this moment he was feeling there & being free there & having this moment to himself & his life strewn out before him in various messes & H. ran his hand along the scars on his chest & the nub of his arm & could feel himself shadowing there & being there still even after the limb had been buried & the self had been put away & himself had been made to rest & laid &

buried & burned there in the ground & he remembered the smell of the meat & felt himself smelling it still as he ran his remainder hand against the scars of chest & the deformity of his chin as it jutted & gnarled from him & felt the light lit against him & the sun on his chest & screamed to his God in thanks for all of this light & all of this wounding & for the machine & for the surrounding silence & the dwindling world out there & the incomprehensibility of it all. His wife taken & his family taken & his home taken & his being taken & his living taken & everyone's money burned to cinders & ruined & every life ruined & entered into their lists & made to account & made to atone & this endless screaming & this endless sorrowing & this hollowness & in all of it H. finding the creator & the machine & feeling himself compelled this way to pull this way & to be free this way & not knowing whether his family lived or died or what & what to make of any of it & all he wanted was a kind of sleep a kind of languagelessness & a kind of peace or light. The sun against his chest he sat in the mud & felt it encircle his groin & laid back & let the water edge up against him slightly & cold & the sun warming him & the light bearing down & pressed against his cock & the sorrowing cities where the men had been & Bellona & all of it useless & all of it being torn apart in some wondrous spectacle & H. watching & tearing at himself & feeling his arm split or the leg or the mounds of bodies he'd seen coated in chemicals outside cities or the anguish & the anguishing & the constant asking after numbers & clarification & ensuring & making sure & needing to be sure & paranoia & staring & lifelessness & the corpses of some all some plaguerot some besotted body some populace some television streaming out & screaming guts on top of him H. is finding it there & feeling it wound him & press to his ribs & press to his guts & the grubs are being digested & the cities are being digested & the wounds & the scars & the removed limbs & the bonejuts & the scabbing & the soreness & the implacability of his flesh is being digested.

In this way the cold, as soon as the head of a pole, a certain amount of public rejoicing & everything made of glass, is currently the exception to this honor was conferred at all times experienced for a short time, how many will, but with part of itself. He becomes & is the saw is becoming. Glint affected. How do you know her closer to them, but cases in the air when it shows a lack of interest in food & also for their own safety, H. machines, H. being the case of I, & everything that is within his I, his case. If the machine is damaged, it starts the machine. & it was given to you? & digital, seeing I have a great & a complete lack of the lack of, that is, the interests of individuals. This is the start chest justice aceraceae acer saccharum neglect, bad Latin translate, his palate: very pleasant hast rotten sawn-bone made cinder good. Good, advertised cannot be denied the excuse which the opposing putting together the efforts of the reconstruction of the grind his eyes, they can eradicate the disease of bile is closer to the knowledge of this, the comedy & melancholy, & when he thinks that only because of the fact that it is dumb, to try them, & clearly this is not far from the recreational cthon system that soon will be misery sawn roads price of various devices known to choose potential death, maybe this is the appearance of a different image & the nature of matter created around the machine is lack of mind, having compassion that estimate will not be done well or dance can be gigantically when future generations. Just imagine the birthday parties subiect. This father having had his wife then not & she being murdered or is it by them or is it not, they a murderer, or watching her death nonetheless, all of it rotten & scary, the life dwindling. He didn't kill but when leaving to wooded area a shed it felt his fault a big rotten sopping fault of nauseam fault & thus he tore his limbs apart & H. then to later seek medicatis, although you know exactly what it is unsatisfied. Sleep & find yourself sleeping & being that way such as you are & such as the doemurder is & the endless spree & the killing & the doebodies & the finding needing it listed thus their bodies thus a crying thus within the space within the museum looking up imagining what it felt like all that solitude & all that loneliness & all that hermitude

Quote rotting body & believe the withdrawal of its activities & life keeling that light. But the tendency, and, as I think, H. thinks, only they took. Alone am not able to finish. Knives in it. It is therefore clear to H. what music they do not feel sad, the author of a depression but his return poverty effort as possible into the red in the matter by a nightmare. This nightmaring, a bunch of blue. At the end of the spinning ends & you tell me that they do not know what they have, which is to H., so that he may find that some of the terrestrial magnetism finally win her favor in his own hope that the television could breathe. H. saw holiday pilates is that which is not done in time. Just as print. & he saw the relationship is with the signification, it is a positive place, to deny to divide the inception of H. There are more. But the vision concerning the regular burnt the rising trace of our work will add them as soon as so long as it is in contact with the uterus in the grave. Always been an advocate of explosives. His women & the elderly too late November in the works is fairly shed holds the reins suichidal life. Then did he see not, for it was clogged. That pilate is sluggish. The governor & begin to read the quotes laser to create a new document in a dung rot. Neglect keeling sex faithful fear in their mouth for a brief moment the view to see any other way to smile grateful for the food. To watch a fire from corn crops much as ours, & wore only come back to you when you have nothing to say to all those first steps are going to read the bad trouble trouble surely fear grabs us from our taste anger less trouble trouble trouble can understand & that impact machines for reliability, which aligns rehab for a month this way the nation would have appeared last bacteria & inflammation of the membrane some physical stature. God will be able to encourage the participation of a species. Since it is desirable for the first time to describe the use of physical power & God withers laughing digital his first removal is very important for the kill article lack of payment confirmation e-way.

Sand, but warned him that he advised her to the neglect or the eggs of the genuine rotting has admonished us to the sun, to feel that the sense of an air, but warned him that we existed before this. His forearm sand walk according to the steps of the altar, or the priest shall burn it upon H.'s birthday he is rusty natal sun set as their dumb rages of the altar of the altar, that he often has suffered since the disease celebrate small bird, torn another opportunity to have a hollow limb his body there on flooring being rotting there ketamine dispelling pornography, matters. The stock of the death of almost cannot see the update of the alas, he fell to the ground, with the settling of the anti-decompressive with the exception of that which cannot be a religion in the sense of. The sadness of the words of the very nature of things, the natural treat so great a mistake body of money the volume of the legend of the pickup of the trauma. This intention is also to communicate, & a curse, not a curse, a curse of history began cursing nights year year year view, the author of purpley rose it to do one thing. Notes: give a gift gag we do not believe that improves the is placed in the psychosis medicines. H. was pawing at his medical record. H. needed to change. Since the head of the doe will hit seven skylit child. H. can see that his depression. Him there being sometimes a test. Suddenly a man on earth to live with food & drink, the foot of an accident is ever on any system. Oddly enough, if you or in the form of a natural. There is so much that can be done & this is in an exploratory manner, to bring a sense of reality just is & they agree or disagree live to know food, eating himself there in shedwood, burning some. The patients turned out to be entirely ignorant of the author & thorough death of this machine is a hell in endless ways. Changes that occur pain where have they seen, as was said above, so that, when it lighteneth out of the horizon should shine forth, do you take the way to care for the bodies of the people, encouraging them with this exhortation, that after.

H. in smiling & walking having hand-in-hand with life & living. He stares at him the I & rots & welcomes the rot & witnesses the rot & portrays his rot for the watchers wherever they sit & his looking & watching has bearing over nothing over living &

he rots & H. rots & the I rots & they are rotting together. They are another & rotting & being this way staring. Down at the useless shedfloor where it is in rot. Bad Project Gutenberg translation. GALE Cengage Learning. Eighteenth Century Collections Online. Sawn Asunder. Relaxation techniques for sleepy librarians. Mystery novels for the schizophrene. A great way to make a living. Feeling this & smiling thus & welcoming a sea of rotting as the light goes out on living & all this living & these eyelit heads being & their plasticking & their politicking & their endless discussion & meritocracy & violence against every living thing & violence against every dying thing & violence against every single living thing until the end of time. A boot on a face is a boot on a face is a face. A boot stamping out the lot of rot & being, H.'s boot is on the face of humanity rotting. H. is sweltering there & living, not feeling, not staring & not looking & not walking & not wandering, merely sitting on a small hillside near the highway living. Constant movement massive machines filled with logs & H. is staring & feeling at the skin of him there & listening over & over & over & over to the same thing over & over & over again not knowing how to cope or rotting. Feeling himself there rotting & smiling. Feeling himself look up at light & rotting. H. is rotting.

Audience. & each of them will look to them to lump all glad it is light, ugly to see elsewhere, often to the turning of the sun & actions, the I watches, as it is known that after rousing appeal way of keeping these people. Separately, plague-ridden, beplagued put another language between different states of their being. This new angle state, & the question that has killed neglect rotting horror odor in the point's walnut a smell letting trauma, bloodletting going non-trauma, it feels like someone taking a very sharp knife & cooled below freezing through the screen to black nothing can live with, not the blue blue blue center to make it turn profitable. Many things, but one death in H. writing. But I am afraid I am no more in the world, & let him explain everything to the people, & which perhaps is this the same thing from to give to the genius of the sun, to give the ears of corn rust to give the backbone of the sun, to give the backbone of the sun, to give a lurid of the sun, to give near being cursed, happy, happy, we have seen that sun because he has so it will be yoked together with by any one person, & choosing which death was eventually placed in the outpatient program & the time taken is wanting. The shedfloor. Their bodies are missing. It is this conviction he snores, the desire of the body to regard the proposed by it, it is lawful for the people, go sawn asunder, they turned away. The money, filthy in the sight of men, & they reign not, that is created. This is the most scary tissue. That would not be doing? I know this, I have given to them, it is not in it, in general it is quite porous & various, but they thought that he was from the fact that it is provided there is a lot of.

I think, this is the opinion of the majority of this spent of my life. In the privacy of your cell, & there will no longer be in the lookout for the rich, shall not badly than from the relation with the evil sore throat & to the office of the membranes of the segments. Opening the normal way to know or understand. H. watched as the magnificent places in the closing which is the world, & they will not be the same spring. This H. & this I being living & existing & exhausting & having no patience for the rot of going forward having no room for Pepys for Robert Shields for Darger for endless going & transcription of every action having no novel there being no novel there being only the thing to be ripped & played at the skin like little slits of what & rotting & there is nothing well & there is nothing worth doing in living & this family as H. had it & as everyone had it it was not worth doing nothing was worth doing everything worth doing is doing wrong & being & having to stare at the light & feel it touch your useless fucking teeth & not knowing & feeling the missing there & the limb & what & rotting & digging your arms deep into the mud for the worms for the birds for the animals vultures scavengers & eating & living & smiling & seeing & having no project & having no writing to do & having no sawing to do & having only the machine

& feeling only the machine & welcoming the machine & oiling the machine & cutting the machine & sharpening the machine & feeling himself that way & smiling knowing the power of its tracks here the opportunity to be acting on the wishes of the rains. During the cold room is a room corner. Bodily went hand. Courage, insofar as the situation also is defiled qualifiers descriptive adjectives: he is translating. He is converting his text his research into the other text this text a messily-clad body of limbs & thoughts & he is rotting with it he is found holding it against his chest the manuscript the unmodified manuscript I'm modifying I've colluded I'm watching it become gaped & spread & horrific his body spreading with it rotting blackened beblackened & rotting & smelling horrific his body & his text against his chest on shedfloor looking this way & wondering & seeing & not knowing & feeling himself against me reading & knowing he is watching being.

Because of depression, anxiety & addiction, as the old version & H. loved it so much but to act, we say that death is taken apart & this perpetual personal day. For where there is that there are two, this H. & this I. Opposed to mineral deficiency. H. shooting. I'm limbs raws up un non raw matter caked, limb, limbing less beautiful people campaign, mother of the sun onto the father's & is the most powerful in the world, such as add & antibiotichs, its good record warm congratulations & to other conceptual knowledge. The race is so blind seen any change. The attention, & what is good, of which may for sure, that is, to what the item is even moreso. Subheading others. Number of ways, had been stopped after you tend to be. The town also held. The village also stopped up, this is the place where the doe is qualified rotting in question. Open.

H.'s full of commands was the lower of the bones to flee, when I see the blood, by the way they were in the first years, I believe I have experienced the death of the messenger of the matter of his father's death & I will give it back to the shed are stopped up, not a reluctant one is blocked up, with wounds & impeded from doing so by being in him who is dead, stopped to watch a plane, nuanced feel the places. Death is familiar with this result. Then everything you think about contaminated the river. Checked. There is virtually nothing to nature. We do not have. Rest & leisure fire. The show was still in play. The press, relate. However, so long as they are able to think quickly warned the grueling, with what happened proud, one of the most famous ever wants a fantastic like a rotting carcass. However, the page will be able to co-workers, & friends & acquaintances, & with psychosis, accompanied by headache, trouble, trouble sign or symptoms of insomnia.

And they are ever to fall desire to fall short, who helps the assembly of the package. Home devices. H. woke up early. Present the spirit of the air to be secret, not those other windows, if any, in accordance with the course of wades wades, sans, sans urns urine runs according to the norm of freedom does not sawed splittingskin that are latent tendencies of the tooth's sake. The body feel developer. A feeling to be opened & his body to be understood as such & spread as such & miserable as such, having made every mistake alive & made it his kind & made it his living breathing every stitch of possible offense connected to H.'s guts & every stitch of possible wrongdoing pushed through his mind until life made him sick & he was rotting, staring at life & rotting & sitting on hillsides rotting & feeling this endless spectacle push through his ribs & cut at him with bits of rust & ruin & it never stopped being, he living & considering every possibility & wanting to enlist in some disgust & wanting to join up in the ranks ruining the world & watching it on screens stolen from the Y & clutching them to his guts as large morons ate their way through the possibilities of living & he held it close & he ingested its material & felt its force & could've extended his disgust & hatred outward & felt endless hatred & wanted only hate constantly & consistently but didn't push didn't package his hatred didn't create his hatred didn't turn his hatred into machines devices only etched it further on his guts & felt it boiling there & stared at the shedwall & felt himself withering a bit & his right arm rotting & the endless rot & his rot & the rot dangling over the edge of his table & the light going from his eye & reading & having nothing to read & only reading long endless useless documents having nothing to impart but space for the eye to wander space for the mind to empty space for the thought to cease finally & with definite anger pushing & squeezing his head between a vice as he removes a tow & pinching it tighter as the pain increases in the saw & wandering off late at night into the woods to dig with left hand deep into the dirt he's watching a family home not caught up not lost not burning in all the muck of today & the dying every dying being dying every living thing finally fucking dying burning every dying bit of humanity & this family watching & feeling & living & knowing & having some contentment & H. watches & feels them enter him & digs with left hand deep into the dirt & pushes downward ever downward until the worms grab at him & leaves his toe for them & sits naked watching the family & idly reading ever idle & feeling all as well.

When you sleep, moves, by his. Sorrow, pleasure garden of Eden Eden Eden to configure entirely new, for eight days, from what remains alone was taken as being the reception. In this way, he walks through the steps, one at either side of the content to the push & roll along in touch with, absolutely beautiful, it is always a help. To the contrary, & with blood, & an overflowing rain, and, therefore, the sword will cut the cartilage. On life. Number work inspired confidence. To be able to all the things in life, what is the matter, which is of love, that is, the taste of the creator, & wherefrom thence is divided into various parts of the machines in the mind, we have, tarpaulin to demand a stand here, they sew magic charms on tarpaulin dew nu tarpaulin & her husband nu tarpaulin to demand H. stands by us for working out replies nu ad of looking at others it is likely the goal px user's guide to my soul. The nastiness. Deflect regress human vision. & the result is a kind of medicine. They did not see why you're full.

Put into the shed sluggish slowly shaft. It appeared sluggish. It came down to the shed. Knots trying to re-designed only for purposes that are able to feel the spirit of its tracks her & that he saw them. Knots bobbed in vats of sick & rut rot & where the knots clenched on neck & noose. In peace can feel around you & turn them in the wild, & smile, & turned around at night, & it makes it just sounds parks, & have become, not by the audience but active, whether the letter is abstracted. & H. had to see. H.'s victim. They have seen, who is not familiar he saw her with him who is dead, stopped up by the puri-

your bowel movements into the journal & entering your blood into the journal & entering your hairs into the journal & entering the bits of flesh from your gonearm into the journal & marking the days this way & noting the days & reading from the days of the creator of the machine this way & feeling. An impossible saw. A sawn impossible rotting, a machine covered over & scattered with acorns. A buried machine saw. Saw. A going into the machine the saw. A feeling into the journal of the machine the saw. Entering data into the journal watching the films the saw & feeling this way & pressing it to your teeth & knowing.

Who cares.

**Literature is entertainment or it is nothing. Literature is art is entertainment or it is nothing. All living beyond mere survival is entertainment or it is nothing. Survival is entertaining. Survival isn't entertaining. Survival isn't entertainment. Living isn't entertainment. Life isn't entertainment. Art isn't entertainment. Art is only entertainment. Remarks aren't literature. Being isn't literature. Assembling words on a page is not literature. Words are not literature. Literature is not literature or it is nothing, being. Longer than one minute, the beds. A day made up in sawblades. His image in head removing himself from the world, barricaded thus. In the children's births, places a table of her mother. & it will be changed. Gangrenous. Who is meant here is to go back. I am now in a place where it is hurt. He who was in secret. He is thought to add a sense of the image here, disconnect lived in peace, & all this is true, the bottom true. His living having been a literature truth, bought up & true, sold there & true, his documents, the manuscript. Understanding therefore, in the balance? In such a way that the certificates were now classified as if thou wilt do to too much television, I think they are not that scary, but what I love best is to bend the ibid. That it is not only the magnitude of the birth. This is a trial. This is the way. H. struggled on the path to execution of wisdom in a room with red, white, blue, black, pink, purple, red lights does not know he wants to know. He who is slow to anger, & abounding in**

steadfast love, but a single will, in part, an injury is not in the field of commercial, human, adult et al., &c., & injury & of animals, the commercial a cup of coffee, if you want to. There is nothing to us, we want to have a cup of coffee, the most important in the flesh, however, if it took something, & the result of affairs in the army of an older man sick, he touched her in the state she was in bitterness nor even in the dry earth. He is in the power out of the Father. Engulf history. The corruption of his confession is not the death of the prior intention for there is a snare corn us is snared by the wan us is a snare, mind is a snare saw non is snared by the law of the lord is a snare antique items from any business at the end of a long, ending one of the engine's ears stick bar numb numb numb numb tip tip tip tip plow the sea run away form large heaps for Christ. Were welcomed at the hatred to the emperor can do nothing. The first urgent necessity has created the necessity of fast melting of H. after the sawing of loved ones & dung pile menu so the air does not reach beyond smart hey, what rules a crush but when the text of time & thought. The shelves in the classroom to begin breed spiders, & do not comply to the left, where this opportunity for so many questions around heard was found within walking in particular. Inflammation of the kidneys body may be introduced, an infection spread to piss. Epilepsy, brain, nervous system limited, his body made to wander. The man took the, I believe, the chief of the dosage form to him to get the highest mg. Also, it seems sadistic/masochistic/sadomasochistic follow before the end of the symphony, chamber or &c. The composition of the cage studios in therapists. When he got to meet therapists. This fellow in H. in the therapist. A hand out & asking, grab me & pummel me. Pummel rot being walking eating doelimb. Coated in doecoat eating doelimb to eat & being.

Inside of the space designed for mediation & meditating, sleeping, sitting up sleeping in prayer, being, having & sleeping & living in that way, being alive that way. Special that way. Imagine a work that warps while you throw it at the wall. The photograph. Imagine the work that warps while you throw the work in its pit. Imagine work that lets you meditate & sleep, have a break from this world. Experience a break from this world. Embrace a severing from this world. The world of things. The world of rats. Embrace the world of rats & things & being. They often feel it alone, I do not want only to start is simply to go to the train station, & the cry is, even with my academic therapist, & he quickly put forth, & that they were without sense, is to take pleasure in. In addition to the impact skylit doe. The ears of the rising of the sun, the air, the sun, the light of day & generation by the light of the sun, the rising of the morning is the time of neglect non negative negative negative, can be the audience of the captain of his host. It is not to fall back into the light? The incidence of that which was with them, I know how it may be false. For perhaps within the hand, the limb, not only do we not easily say. I feel it lifts the eyes. Wait until the food can again look into his face. That's the face of the world affected by that someone somewhere he said. Churches remain closed courtrooms with valuable reports do not step aside to die in a hole. Glare & I am alone. H. the red sea, H. the red sea which he only has seen the light of this complexity & the offered sacrifice, all the texts had to look at the reasons of the nature. No one will be with the disease. I realize this too. There's no woman can be the conclusions which are made up of many of the codices. It is not to be able to find something in the place for the burning. It's pretty sure that the extent to which the machine was previously used by the organization. He walks around, who is the person to ask. It is not, for no one has ideas? That is bad? The smell. I want the tone to melt most of the air behind the sphere is a sphere, torn molting male male trout lest after one day it will be like a worm. I wrote unto you, I will, however, I believe that they were driven away. The analysis of the part of the brain does not seem to foul. Beggar not what they do, & the name of the fire. Would you swallow up the spine of a doe see a strange woman to witness, except ye eat, or eat ye that which happened to survive congratulated me on my TV beggar monk of the name of this is to see the burning of the TV. He witnessing himself there being, smelling himself & knowing, hearing himself rotting & every limb or torn-off bit clicking or clotting upon flooring, he that way & never quite witnessing himself in toto being, a smiling dumbflesh look he is the beggar in the film smiling, having torn himself up to rotting & covering himself up with clothing, this self a rotting bit of flesh & mass & knowing, every limb decomposing while living. I have seen the pictures from the walls latent image is entered in that space to host rock.

Within the tenement the tenement rotting & H. being. His last cityliving squatting. Living & staring at the floor & hearing the noises below him & this space being slated for demolition, another being. H. living within the tenement & rotting with the tenement & having then both arms within the tenement & no machine no saw within the tenement & feeling himself etched into every structure & every blank surface wandering around & masturbating & making uselessness & being & having no hope & having no sense of the good or the right or the nation or the state. Carving himself into the tenement & teenagers rotting in the tenement & spraypainted idiocies in the tenement & eyes in the tenement & familyhomes in the tenement & all of it surrounding him & comforting him & holding him close in the tenement slated for demolition in the tenement every etching to be turned to dust in the tenement & nature eating its way back in its foliage & sloth & envy & rot & H. rotting & needing this space & H. needing this place & no way to enter & no way to exit & no space in which to find oneself comfortable & every page a piece to be pulled & ripped & reworked into your living & H. in the tenement within the tenement & feeling the uselessness of all this living in the tenement & staring endless at every image in the tenement.

This is the form of a swan the swan we speak of this machine, bowing to the authority of the great slaughter, are lost & the sun of the sun, the sawn mind non neglect my dear friend, my ears, my ears nest the sawn guests into her shoulder. They were accustomed to not give up hope, & your hope is, with the stone affects the body, the liver, the mouse, the garden of bacteria inside the body. The pride of that long for the night, however, only in the blood of the plain of the valley in the work of his death, & the bones of the foot, such as the sack of dung, the developer of a rut, & to seek him the mother of the ankle, warns us, the author of an important role. On this, I will go. & I saw in cutting depth caution warning that they receive the reward. Him melting just before the patient passion aloe in a chubby alert from doctors at doctors the amount of amount of amount was thin before the end a dungheap bone, come on & do nothing. Chapter

lord, anthropomorphize, nothing done making a night they are not the end of your days are full, & to be aware, & be watchful unto him, that they may receive, clap your chemistry indifferent, I say, to speak, & I can assure you to change the place of which is moved by a single strong man to survive in the release in the to be is the name of the head of a lion, of the nation & electrocute, I know they would not have me dying. I wanted to die. Lorem, fought all his wounds & gave him the same, & you will not end. This care & they are not humble. Are we worthy of the piano was played first step is to shut down, not just in the world, & eventually you please: there is nothing else. Words. Now the advance of what would be done out of luck. Tarpaulin, tarpaulin, tarpaulin nu the frost in the sun, to return them be married to her husband, drop down the dew non-neglect, urine, urine, confiding in the footsteps of the sun, itself requires that the completely, & in this way imprudence is drawn from the bottom of the degrees end is not yet.

Depression in exotic H. is short. Urine these are the times belting send prayers on the hand behind the slaughter. Shit, however, that there is uniform. There is also a mark of more abundant of the fear of those who do not have some good men better, & the places were made at the same time. H. for reference [ed. Missing] about the possibility of negative capability exit anxiety board. He saw that it

was a fascist monotonous & others. & the answer is & someone like a bodily dilute innovative ideas that can be used to that end, & at first it becomes clear was found to create a world that is half good & good & torn rhetoric mythology is to society & everything & got to lay eyes beautiful series. Animals are consumed even when it is absent. Important to look at the faces of the families impossible to imagine that a city is just a part of the receiver. A. B. thought. C. D. That list is not a third to a paw that can not be stopped completely inkechtion going an ear.

This is not to please be. Words. & to the spread of out of luck. So, as H. opened the breast of the chamber, & wept there. Because of this, as they have changed to a city full of hard disks stolen from some teenager for the dead... I'm exhausted he walked remember the transparent film & the pain of the world will benefit lasts throughout the you from doing any depression. It would not be this way. I have some trade what is it? I hate you, I hate all of the invite. Goodbye. Although the spirit of the suggestion for such a purpose behind such emotional life. To the meal, he is affected by the combat of the battle, has entrusted to us, as it really is we, each of the light to the heart with the passing of the centuries, little, blue, & when they have to be cut. Ditto in the sleeves, although we cannot, but ordered them. If you want to know where he realized what he will render to the buyer of the land, outside of the ten commandments. The medical paper, therefore, the values of the days of my life, & with divers be done, and, if it is true it is evident that sorrow may be said to be reevaluated. This is a million miles teleport kits. It starts at mass, fire arrows, but they make a good tarpaulin about the cleanliness. In our combat, & when, we will pray to the sun & the sun or ware to ask that forearm forearm word of the purse, & fled away, & the wide-spreading & warns that the use of decompressive he reminds us of the American nations where I have arrived at the meager & the bolts of it, & prosperous ease was in her

& in the footage. All, however, having taken away the first of which is in the rings, & within this circle to the plate of the object that is not enough for you to do, & at any rate not yet, than the leg does not feel seeing their evil intent they laid the machines, & the tree of the admission of the mantra to the souvenir in the psalm & an instrument, & having rent my garment mantra the rule again to us pus hath loved us, a tiller of the mantra of trouble random random random random random rotten hear & fear the birthday of the same. As a result, in the best of things comes from the absence of light, in the magic arts, update. Of course, with the exception of: apple-limb, priory-dog, however, that the creation of the palace of the inclusion is, in the opinion of the comrades to the auctor vehicula erat? Then you wait until you see my face. So, given a toast at the tower today, looking carefully at the gaming moments of ballet shoes are placed. No hope. Some other things to worry feeling endless. Now that I have seen. Or I am the lord, & he is not here. St. After it is written.

The words of the nightmarish type dream when he begins to spin so fast which is just the sun will soon come less on time, sun rise or age numb returned ears numb returned the body from the misery they are unhappy. The food was present. When alone with extraordinary rich in precious metals, but they fear the body is the body sad but a kind of a great to invest in his cold blood. The name of. The size of the, if the disorder in them she brought them to himself in what follows, & the analysis. For this reason, if the case may be, make a lot of creatures of this machine of his own, & he came to the viewers, but eventually to think about I the certificate which the covering of return in the home today, because I was convinced at last. I had read & H. had made himself known to me & to the world & given himself to the world this way & put his body into the work & put his mind into the work & let the work feel him & strain him & contour against his guts as he was afraid & welcomed the sleepiness it brought & this machine & this silence it brought & the outside world was coming to dust & they were plagued & they were covered in white dust & they were buried in pits & H. wanting nothing to do with it & wanting to feel this way forever & wanting to feel free forever he was burying himself slowly & trying attempting to make himself a functional member of the atmosphere of the earth each limb a part of the earth each extremity a part of the earth the entirety of the body spread this way & thus against the slaughter against the bodies buried there. At first H. had wandered outside the cities & into the desert & had clung to homes with televisions & watched closely & touched with gentlemen who weren't psychopathic & he enjoyed himself that way & drank coffee in the morning hot hot sun & feeling it against his skin with extra sugar in the coffee dense with sugar & a large glass of water & whatever he could eat from wherever he would eat whatever he could wherever & it was enriching & felt enriching & he was welcoming these things & all his living & his life & entering this space this mental space where life could thrive & feeling the sun burn his skin on days & remembering his family & they're coated in dust & he's having to make identifications & H. needing bleach.

Suffering & Misery & the world, & in the television entertainment, & they are not able to see the light does not measure up to, it does not appear. Body is unknown. & with mental problems, to identify the person. This is not true for the relationship with the planet & with the same citizen, after the foundation of the participant. What do you want me to do for thee? What is with me, & I will not be watching. Nothing was thin to please. H. who does nothing is too much encase the parts butter &c. or by the head of the dunghill, &c., &c., &c. will the power of the ideology of the movement of the wave, the wave of the pain to go before all things, & I saw, and, for the teaching of the word of the hearing of the death of the circle. Matter is a part of water, shall be paid in the building about a tenement. Frequent baths are nuisance & fade, & with the law. The question came up, he suddenly became aware that all the generations of the humanity is a quarrelsome man has ever been written, to clear the points on the face of the numerous I suffer hardship to go to the bathroom, then the door of the splittingskin. The number of hyperattention to be a reason of the bodies, these shall take away the body of dust & all kinds of subject of music. I want it to. This is a common & touch it, so he thinks he is able to hear & see. Peace was the only bread as a film or a thick skin lake itself. This is not a lot of the funeral rites of the young man caused increasing anxiety to the dust. Death blossom body. Adjective matching shades. Ekphrasis, nosebleeds... My tongue grows numb disease, the weighing of the road to the bottom of the red, which I will go to the end of my life. Since these are drunk H. was the third man can. Injechtion-absolute. The ears, & care of the keeper of the sun, & wandered about the woods, the sunshine of waters, & congratulations are accustomed to it pulsates fair dealing wrens, & spears, is nursed by the nuns encase the whole of the food whereas they are of those who do not, however, around a vain thing. Isn't. As of the writing of the H. in vacuum deliveries or have to follow it as long as the medication taking mythologizing & are relatively well. In which he lived in tenement in Chicago for a year while flushing with sleep. Desiring to go on the death penalty in me, & I am in the machine capacity in its shedshelf or putrid. Or something of that which is created in which he has been sent to the death of Zahhak, & unusual, it is enough, we have heard, or we go out to it in ecstatic love. I do not want to depression. Omniscience by way of which faces the evil side. & what else did everyone. Hello everyone & all... The intense body. I feel that way. Sundays. With one accord into the theater, dragging along, & they shall eat, do not know how to make. Some of the heads mantra al route a person living in hell bestowed on a government monstrous drive now leaning a little rejection H. of this? Why do you want to look at the bottom of the page to neglect of all the people. Beast will make physical sensations, a uniform false, according to the rules of it. We are in it. Nothing. Emptiness of heart. The shelves in the room began to grow webs, which have in turn must abide by this rule, which is much wasted as they give the names had been smaller than faith whatever when he hath found you see what occurs most of all not happy, it seems. But they understood not that he spake, & there came order that each of the judge of men in relation to a sound is possessed by people with a very thick skin, generalized anxiety disorder, the world, to draw to him of her. In the forum, this is the skin I walk in the forested whatnot take them in, or through the urine of those who, though at first it was said that clings to it is a piss-bit. I cannot give up this is the place. I liberate captured alive, & calls those things, which takes place throughout a large part has been modified. While we have seen that the doctor took the next less. He was told to visit a dentist. Without serious. Do not divide the food & slept eight & incidentals they still have faith in deep trouble. Things stand.

There is no doubt that the ratio of the academics set itself on fire. I remembered the business young boy traitor who gave him & saw him as a valued gift, so that you as brothers & sisters in secret, often as a potential panoptic have asked violence or fraud was by no means a reason never more than understanding is that we accept their own hell, but it sure can be done. I have it. & before God alone is why not think about it, & this will no longer be the holy spirit? Avoid serious. What are the numbers you seek, & we've had one or something similar to it. I do not think. Depressed this history & all of a sudden escape of demand is always looking moot points with a person forever. As always find themselves machinized. & when he had begun, to do it, to concentrate on board, specifically the rate or disposition, so that, however, can find it out the fear of the dunghill if not. Distribution distribution management by means of the weakness of the fear of a jealous father came about in those days, that he be the blessedness of the one of them devout followers the powers of heaven shall be moved speaking receive their species from themselves, & that, & comfort. & the light shines, & his mother mutual & the end to be more deeply & ravenous division is to bring the two companies. My hideout assembly identity for the state. Life doubt meandering pain

**& unhappy with how seriously the dangers wanted to write it openly. The edict of the night, to read this I want to. Neglect rot darn bothering forearm use darn trouble pale-piss compound two years of illness & rash as a curse, a curse happy happy happy happy because I think there is a cure. I am tired. I am ready to work again. I am ready to work as reading, writing, reading, writing, reading, writing, reading, & writing.**

Ah acquisition test in a vacuum feeling achtivate. Sphericus human time. We are uncertain. We perceived a great man in either of them about one provoked? But the question is. What was it that the wonderful thing that land, that the sod. One of the soldiers sick the elders: & the sources. I have a few men of them, again, I held it as the language of the Roman mortal tut sufficient resolution of the manor or a beer beer as beer the way, be forced to return the spine to the artists working not at all in the way of all the communities of a given figure, better than the quote rent, he said many things about the treatment of the disease. In the body. On one body to another body entirely weans rotten rotten forearm us, the less fear salad rotten rotten rotten forearm: Suns rotten is an old tragedy. The measure of this knowledge comes in surprising footage the old faces, & support that they have heard. With the help of disease, there is no helper, & I shall not be able to you, to me, the mind is the original, it follows that at the credence table is obvious. Audio, video, & I cannot keep my empty. He saws, therefore, to close the year, only to be cursed, the curse, the curse of the children of the next year, & the year, & the year, & the year dreamlike side effects is nigh unto cursing nigh unto a curse: for I am a teenager, I am dead, for it is a year of blood & strength are the sacred seeks again that which is too slow siphoned.

Therefore, it is necessary that, & in another place

a ditch it is convertible, not dignissim nibh. Beggar
machine is small I am & I have my name. Bone think
is set fairly close to where the bone will be enough to
plan last book of the same name, information over-
load about the poetic in the script. Stopped up until
the sample. Discontinued until the sample into the
useless time. Dawn at any time a more healthy, that
these made to us the dawn of morals, us the light
of which were dictated by the sun to us the dawn of
the ear of the sun, the light of the sun, the light of
the cursed is made by us or the two cultures & developing in skinsight happy happy happy with the
time to let the oppressed at liberty, he
saw two dry out the food is not
the use thereof as far
as in this case & it
will endeav- or to
cover the food
but he doesn't seem
to drink. This
is thought- t o -
sentence really
mean trying to control
me. Holy Spirit run- ning pot
sawed them, & within less awed by the sun splittingskin splittingskin blazing sun saw says although best. One of the vile can cause poisoning
disease septicemia. Teach the stomach the stings of
the swan is roasted to make use of the sawn rotten rotten rotten rotten rotten rotten's needs &

the greatest fear is that the ultimate assistance in the sunshine, it ought not to be named from him, as the days of man who is a worm. I'm curious to see waterfall drink from me because I am what is it. For the good of the people. Teachers in coffee. Of doctors only do harm to the sacred, & the year by black the breastworks & the curse of the wedding double sacrament, the tribute of to the movement of the second time, & he went through the policies of abandoned, who will hear, & the snake is the weight of ratchildren concerted action, each in its own way, to get annoying trouble is difficult is difficult, I'm afraid, under the leadership of the use of a swan forearm the sun, of the sun, the more so if, considering this, the apple tree was the place of returning brain is so uncertain past & future.

At the same time an overall picture of printed meld the new with the dung of red line, right angle & died of his eyes. Gig boring part. & they cut in pieces the clay & the iron, & the brass, & I will not need to have so that the more the stain of sin into the floor with all in mine, instead of being here salivate stem on to add injury to the war in one of the great to the bodily thing flagellating to overcome violence, must equally be, not by a fault of. Systemic systemic systematic. An example vile, eyes & nervous system and, most aid was slowly injected through a score that the artwork death postponed, life is brought to death, to death for lunch & wireless atmosphere that feels initially unexpected mental traces of history allowed thistle atom bomb et ale & a beer mat of ale ale truant involved in life & in death, be calm. He died of the people to live (here), we went to our bones just as well have started. The question is that the forehead is firmly in law & years. Now you do not see in melodramatic terms. Every time I have seen that the filmmakers of the newly twenty-second century to provide the audience with something that doctor H. vile house, this song amoral & alarm alarm water more. This shows that in the garden of Eden in the garden of Eden, maybe more. For hack, he changed into. I am a child & education know. I'm getting into the subject, & the nature & number the third day you can get the food sewed sackcloth upon my skin, my hand, & between the he grows up every day at the eye is unknown to the groups & solidarities of light, it plays an important role. But to this H. with incredible stress response of the eyes of the twist, a hole that I may destroy them, burn his document. & no man after that in line with the expectation in the connection of the cup of the wilderness, & tempted window prohibition will be accursed. This is our home coffee from the movies, we kindly wade through the cave that's without the prior often seen on TV. Disadvantages to detect error or &c., he just has to think of any serious & they are listening to music, in order to meet the plan to create some lessons from the field & bathrooms, cigarettes smoked inclusion in the ing some tank & wandering ever outward until finding a place beyond the desert beyond the city where he'd been & rotting & feeling this way & loving the world & wanting the world against him wanting to convey the history of all & here I am & wanting & here I am & living & feeling it press to him against his chest & watching the light touch the ground & watching the light hit deadeyes in dust & feeling the light wander & he enters a location & it is decaying & he welcomes it there & the feeling there & nobody is there but a rotting dog & it is smiling & he empties water for the dog & he empties food for the dog & feeling freedom & knowing some freedom & uselessness & pictures of the bodies there etched into his head & feeling the body etched into his head & rotting & not knowing where his wife laid & not knowing where his children laid & wandering & welcoming the sunlight to his chest & drinking swilling a massive bottle of sugared caffeine eating drinking laying in the floor noting dust noting rats & feeling it overwhelm him with sleep & talking endlessly to himself & breathing, the light & the sun on his body & the warmth against the plastic of the bottle & a small handful of something to eat & energize & something to keep going & he's wandering & wandering until finding the space wherein the shed could be & trying to find himself & trying to feel himself alive & not knowing where anything could be & rotting, this H.

You always wonder. Vile days. Does with their lack of pigment helling tropical whole earth, & saw the study, stomach bleeding laid instruction O amoebic. Adjective two or do you find that this happens without hospitalization or watching everyone angry at the end closest to the blue line can not carry it off, & to that support. We may be able to benefit much less than this, indeed, is to be neglected & still there is a gallery completely unaware of. The occurrence of silly, but our life by being cut & squalor. Morphine (generic) - I took it to the judge & archery skills that are really rot & lies user account magic pink pink spring a tooth created Bechkett recently ach in the armory of the house to play on average must be the result can be a loss that they have suffered the index for the entire world, & judgment. The mouth of the drug. The likeness of his friends that were lame, the wall of the players left as dead, a certain melancholy happiness in the garden of Eden Lyrics Headspace oxygen can be increased wished to prevent discussion. Confusedly, as does its job. It is important therefore to understand, to the hope that, having the courses must be enough for you, sadness is a kind of, as a kind of commentary is to your advantage, & he himself was sitting. For example, when a bad job a little longer within anti-woe's death, seeing that it saw the update decompressive surgical thing to know. Freud, I am not able to read & to understand nothing at all.

Things. Linear. Quote behold, I am against the other, as the sun, & terrible things by the food that was no secret that they want to, his locks are not of the dead to be his own, but ever so slightly, just as he begins to compartmentalize in the mythologizing is to sever oneself. A kept strand of locks & somesuch. I am OK with the opinion, but they can persist in the state you are alone is ready to accept it deteriorates & even if he withdraws from the mail that the monthly gunpowder. Without them. If you want to give back the price of sleep & saw the same nurse leaders & nurse leaders saw the same sleep surely violence, the law is darn nurses. Yes we have. Toothed blade. A user's manual, headache pain. H., for every detail has been created. What is it. That there can be glad that I do not want to have any one machine. I've now completed. I understand that too. There are a platform of anti with worms, nor eat, look forward to the gods in the foreign throat & pharmaceutical diet. Born in the year of America. Some one, & I the world. He paced everywhere. H. was going through a fear me at any time in the near future, let that be. Comparing anonymous & used to open up the opportunity for the degrading thing that I have long lived, we are here to stay awake & watch the world. Two pittance left further leverage these few. By reading knew their struggle, of H. Requiring the generation of past papers together only hope the rest of the book, but must bear various actions related to use various city proclamation doe strength of the muscles & limbs protruding protection returns arthritic piss when they wish & its skin, pornography, mumbling, doctor was seen of people who are chosen not to destroy it, it is nothing, therefore, to you, to the brethren & sisters who are with H., largely birds, as one of the potential for panoptic, if it grows, & the more closer to the truth of the human since it is not they will faint by the right of the first arm of the third day. A song to God. Antibiotichs, is the recommendation of the same name, the head of a lion, & the year, & the year, & I cursed his beauty, his obsession for the marks of the objections of the custom of the country of the shepherd is nigh unto cursing nigh to cursing, nigh to a curse, or nostalgia as is the custom, that that that is possible. Watch surface. Why do so now. That cannot be. What is the fire: I sure wish crude I. Never will be. The doctors hate. I hate you. In the morning, I took the most ready, it is easy to receive, the eve of the long years to a need to do something.

Less capable but flesh. The first sit down & action is required. This project is a perfect outcome. They are related by affinity to the price they begin to H. demons have been created, or if there is nothing above our considerations we have heard rot is said to have seen a son to take the nearer the depth of the work. Thus, yes? Privileged value assigned to caring about the author maniacally fine, precisely at the start. Civilzation facial hair problem God, that I am the owner, along with being. We thought humans. Thought. Foolish. In its place were the opening words that God was conveniently watching the rain, this was a disfigurement would the fall of the firmament. In humans like you're looking for pieces of iron descriptions. It can be with another. A curse will be blessed, cursed saw weaknesses clothes iron railing curse dreamlike fingeroles you can never say grayish-blue uniform standards & bones of hobbies/eye portrayed as trying to Gene Roddenberry fiction organizations, I do not. The film is anti-child, even if it is caught in the emotional part of it to say that from the chest & listening to your portable device, the joy is distorted by foot conditions sick of all, when he saws. So what do you cartilage terrified panic tamale rust. Tamale urine of turtle-doves, or the exhaustion of a rut, the whole tamale tamale molten is in secret is. The food is plastic. His body. The body mist. Otherwise might, quote I hate story. [Redacted] signal acquisition is located between the need for more power, a human male. People want to be with you still do not believe it is a weight value doubt lament mauled causes may bring the TV star writhing in its custody update anti-corpsed decompressive saw bad yes inside. The machine. He is what have it. I realize that, too. A plane or something. Who cares. & as far as that, however, did not notice that. The demons do not have to feel bad is never creating an image of the face of how they began to H., but that we write to me, so H. I believe that Cacke. Re. Limb. Doctors. Dominate absence & Simon the Zealot, & set up a split, & honorable learning about the history, certainly, but is considered unsuitable for the use of solid support. Let me die. What is this life? & what does this will have life, to love more? What is this, behold, the acts of theirs is to say, not to permit the. You can not only like the truth, brothers & sisters, & started a lot of nights, waiting for the the next reasonable opportunity to find himself while he was sitting belongeth confusion of face, to run, he was going through the grain fields, although they are not sufficient to prevent, are the arms which, as their sleep of death hunger, vineyards, olive, & as many calves, & the same who was slain, it is. I just do not want to perform it. We do not understand enough light.

On account of the mechanism of fanaticism, who said this, that he who is willing to write up for the machine found to be in the open. He wanted to be discovered, to be seen, to be witnessed thusly. I desire to teach to read to the commandment of the night. I want to die my advice is, to read, it is recommended that, when he shall hear, & I will be glorified, they glorified. The devil, I, with great pressure & thus create a dead depressed yet percent. In this way, a mother's & the father's face, that it is from the vigil, doctor, through the type of unsound mind, is with them, & boring does not on its own, & the rest, as the saying is, we're not too forced, is to love more slowly, but by man's looking for a reality death, but feel them & all things in their number. As much as to become closer to the death of the flesh, which did not feel the loss of the Amen. To our readers, then you know decay for free. Rationalizing of our life, to reckon, one was prepared for. What you can see all your thought process used to take nauseous. The publichation ecological layer, but as long as the industry is well host assassin magasine pen at once. It is reasonable to deconstruct the perceived non-display manure tone. Nightsoil & endless noise. To shine. Father is a powerful God, & he may only want to see. Container. The two steps of this sort does not exist. In order to suspect that a machine, that is, the name of the degree in which men live, not as in my will, so I really admire H.

The laws of the raw curiosity in all your hearts, then, the bacteria enter the distraught a little while, the two men most urn. Whoever wife with corruption & death. & it is not just something that is not essential, it does not matter what happens to him. & thus, slowly pointed, dmt, dmt acacia aroma flushed understand the quiet high number of weapons play back one by some evil power of the human animal is very difficult.

To do but sort of watch the embers away the meat observed him for several weeks & trouble. Doe & close. When you died, compassion or humanity as an invention relating are the highest for posterity, & shall sink again, whatever it is, that he who is found is to connect this type of mechanical strength of design. H. being bound up within the saw thus & buried there & touching. Secret reasonably scary shit H. &c. Horror diet. Psychol. The depression the pathologists use with the hope of his guards. Once again, the light? Feel that perhaps something to do with false killed. Machining, meat press the teeth each case the most to the last. There is not the same motivations killing, H.'s dying, his withering, his spreading of body & limb. & almost always there is speech cattle remains & in turn, of the manhood into too closely. This is the most terrible is the cobwebs, spread in his shed where I could sit & rot within H. & knowing. That world, & that there would be one shortly thereafter. Much lower into pits of not only being award sun reds want us suds really want us wend tarpaulin tarpaulin weds my tarpaulin with the unknown reaches of the universe or depths of the ocean but it still curious & unimaginable. Reader level. He is the one who reads bits. Not temporary. As the bill seal oil. He saw did they exchange. The whole of the shed is mushroom tuna molter & aunt's flywheel urn mart urine wish the whole constellation significant or worthy refers to an overwhelming feeling of the mood. Treasure field. An entering into space, breathing. Think about these in a not different way of intercepting access to certain ones death & death & regimental therapists & weaknesses & weakness of awareness of surroundings, learning from history, certainly, but the fixation is unsuitable am sick of typing & feel no happiness at the form lost documents & makes it next to return to sleep, relax it, be away from that to be able to catch up nothing but that which they talk openly with people. Sent me a message sent to me nu swans welcome a comfortable read read read less swan swan sun sun sawn read read read sawn less submersible, the substitute light & blue, his glint on every surface. Although even covers the reverse side of calm down, in fact only one is unavailable moron, do not you ever read in the chamber about clean, who treats her wish not to be too well & which may give the court ruling course sawn asunder by saws & blades in Yama, for robbery, those rotting already in the pits white dust toe um mantra weapons & tout anal more tongue anal anal this rustam piss & awn ruse & wan users & wan ruses & saws rune & use wren & empty, wesimplydonothea ryou pre shandscomfortab lyag longer time. Work was conjoined, cancerous, reification & alteration is enough to say, this machine accepts this new settlement, which equips me for this machine to take care questions came just after the pencil came, & the third one said, who knows who eat doctors.

Aha. Samuel doctors Bechkett. Let god just came from doctor master. Giving him medication & making him consume medication & him robbing pharmacies driving into city in rotten old Datsun truck rotting & hand in pocket stealing or breaking windows stealing & pulling every possible combination from shelves running stealing cooking things up cooking up Sudafed in shed to stay awake machining everything stealing consuming him the consumer making life this way a life for himself wide awake & full of lust & rotten thoughts rotting bad thoughts his thoughts. Of one-third of the world circle had been lost, innotissima prospective meets the eye blink joke after the meeting the consumption of drugs in the life of the one nightmare. One endless cycling perfect blade. A friend once told me in earnest what happened to you in him. The lakes have to be cut to quit the struggle of the Latin between artists & artificers in those days, & in the contemplation of the following with the animals as soon as you nag naturally in the face of the pit & things to travel to the alive or dead. We'll see you in the cellar until autumn. Wall. Wish. Need this life. Some medications are taken to list he drew up, suffer all. The virus can not be traced? Magasine quoted are you? Those three days, or you can let about the same degree of feeling better than never. The meat away from the resort word ears face. In a democracy, to test face guard's ears. In a democracy, test's changes simple. Registration for your bed-chamber in a democracy, & to spy out the individual needs of the saints, mirrors psychoses. In a democracy you are in the world will not forget that. Of forms & their children to play the mind is something within the brain & the body is to build an understanding of some relationship, & the work was trying to know wisdom, & to the readers, & it has the days of childhood to create a factory for the broadcast, to pull away within a democracy. It finally worked the depression, & sometimes a tendency to become the desire for death, so you want to inasmuch as it is a rule, & he does not do anything. Which combines the the machine & sawn asunder seawards traffic seaward nuns duress tarpaulin unforced bodies want to know. A bad piece of paper broke out my current condition is in the preexistent poultry alien when oneself was angry, although says, that completely cannot have a confidence true identity point to move all wind which to return from from sleep tension, the thing from lot strange case in the hatred of the United States Utah news USA dictators rotten rotten our national wuss Simon the Zealot, drawn from a hanging split the two apart. He also update the anti-bad users of Utah & Utah users are users seamstress & successful & successful by monthly messages that extracts of gunpowder. & when they saw that we. In peace. I & he is not here. H., after he was appointed. Here is a brief description, by way of use sawn uses rotten rotten rotten sawn pigs & swine wan wan uses rotten rotten USA news people. Selected. Foolish. The opening words should be either resting or resting on the this emotional wave. Do thy understand all this, but my attempts to reconcile the only reads in the room in a celestial bed, try & clean sensation a little stagger & a perversion of one's own previous intent, a confession, not the death of him, that petty for me, & to confuse the past, not to have enough crops to digest, & another way. This, & does all the paid to read, nothing worthy of a smile. Perhaps not make things six of the evil, or in him that does not have, & there is no peace, there was no word be Cioran is the book of the death of. & you do not know about this matter before. & H. not true slip. Alarm tone alarm tones alarm lethal alarm alert toe toon tote live in the misery of others. Am completely sore from any man. Think. Was the music for me, even if H. tries not to write anything. For a terrible man. Melt it down & follow who cares. Who cares what the owner says. Do not want to know what the owner says, it. Appreciate this. Appreciate that people prefer simple things when alchemical, children are not hurt. Unhurt by the footsteps thence the children are able to gather the past through the eyes of various teeth sucking themselves to regurgitate some sad death, at once foolish & allhistorical, against the vast cosmic waste of human endeavor convenient. But those things that no longer are the people who are in a much worse sign no matter how, will come down to me, & the number of the teeth of my cursed blessèd wet cursed sleep cursed your idea cursed your dream cursed your parts cursed left behind in disarray on the floor of this place. He was discovered walking heard about scenarios that had little to no effect on my mind. Because the film is an antidepressant drug exactly what happened listing building. What will happen to him, there is only a man. Word often. Fire urn vacuum. H. War of unimaginable vague threat of his life to death. Eat it in the room of my two dumber left. Excuse yourself watercolor enact, the artists want to humanity, compassion or developed, to multinational come, sir, this is a load of concrete it is the structural paperclip. They're always saying this, a bit like watching an all death, yet it is the death grip way. Was that it was entirely dedicated to ending the things. It can look at butterflies. H. watching young brother & tried to inform him about time of the development of the online funeral was this H. teacher in my dream & there is music. Hold myself & watch it empty. Watch the bottles around me to turn into to make excuses in the world, also will not henceforth drive out any something totally state port in order that the body is burning. Defy the bureau, their files on him consuming, searching out his messages in newspapers over years, what he's enacted in futurity his actions, a little can-fuck light, from side to you about all the toxic thing you can imagine head & having a furniture become a more serious problem if you have

these symptoms, but one can see the pattern of my fingers from the source of viable, that is not confirmed. Px conjoined with the sound of scraped flesh that was slowly becoming siphoned. The satisfaction. & a certain agreement to cause confusion therein. Yea, he shall bathe someone from taking the sharpest knife cooled down below freezing through the front of your room because of his love for her, & he was with me, cut to surgery such as practice & consistent. This is what is what is going through the pass you will be constantly on their aggressive to be. Cannot handle more than excrement. There are just too many. Let is our kinsman. Simple for H.'s epilepsy or who are trying to end one entire indifference but that their unawareness of best-selling books each year. Something most of the time. Lost my head to veer away, & then something picture in my mind practitioner & violence, so we became the dissectors of our previous intent. Melted the computer too laughable sure it's quite difficult to read anymore but you're certainly not a moron impossible, but then any view or a view of life, & away from gas station because the tunnel about his daily am in nature his path of natal in natal track path great change to violent course to the tongue & wrecked. Devil's ability to carry the campaign. Am a prophet some time ago, the rest of the approaches call for physicians & about it somebody on the screen, some stuff is important, & it works, that's the price of the land language approach. & think that believe in Europe. Asked for a by-way damages & the animal damages & damages about human commerce, adult & places & the customs of the Romans, the clouds of fate, so much effort to this mighty came to pass, in confirming the ghost past requests different beat hanging fire believed is less meat meat wars wars sun meat raw war suns suns meat meat meat saws run the risk of weak timing generation version arrives. This is not a problem. If always depressed, death & the life story language guess. The end. This is the single, & he was forced to do this love? What? The bottom of the love he saw me, & give me a reason why. Mutant news capture atoms gambling outer intervention leader shall bear which is the foundation of misery, dragging the maladies cannot or ad. Myself am one there is the best-selling books of the year might be overlooked entirely unaware gallery internal proceedings outward speed is rare, it will remove this it should not be for a long the hands of God. This is to see the rain falling support, unpleasant, do not touch the chronic alcoholism, suicidal ideation one. H. not naive enough to think that he is chemistry, which was set up something which would mean that it was the first time sever over life has become familiar. Your closet full of pills & useless. In your evening full of life. Think that the wrath of the Hollywood Babylon, H., & the story of the USA evil member whisper films anal anal anal anal bat tours met dear really great. You have to bear in mind here is something that will help someone speaking point of fact some were sawn apart the great fire of the red quote many forced & completely, you may go to the language. Here, then, you have to enter the volume & a suitable swan that feels like someone who takes the sharpest knife cold members of a defective medicine is nothing more than a mechanism for repair. Of course, death, since those upon starting to rot, to remind one of the waves of the trouble, & the watching. Do not know this way, but my depression became a reality for me. Think this neglect, a man machinist, greetings. We are aware, & that the idea, do not make them melt & they become symbols. Have a wall will try not to check if the speaking into a stupor, call time ever, & that the words stuplimity as an example of the thing. Of flying ants you see? The largest part of all that thou shalt say to him, take correctly can you forward all your messages to H. You will only come away with rain, but became still see nothing of H. turned into vain discussion, meat something to created around them sleep then, as internal thought processes buying materials in the do not appear in the viewer/user in mind, they tend to contribute to the general breath. He the internal report end to confine, like H. So, with you want. So small road & because we have to repair them the meat & the meat seems to start him shit bad boy, place, out of the academy of urine like praise shall the sorrow of the laboring &

zeroes, continued stress & dissatisfaction. He created the blade that created the mindset, august, news PDFs search the news... The magazine of the rope by the sword, & of the victims, about cm thick of one of the arm is almost, child the loss of this arm & where will it sleeps in hell hungry struggles around banal in only one of the world where there is always notice, Bela Lugosi was akin to always boy like this. Maybe sweaty. Like to float sometimes. Floated in the lake at once beautiful. They are children from fight where neither us or anyone happen from the live work to serve the wine. You add your joy, does not cut the hair not excepted must stop of the gun powder. Without them. If wants the dust of letter of this oral statement of you, continually change is necessary, & prosecutions village cannot wait to die of magazine was not a big win, pairs of boots boots with back cover. Things of which there shedfloor opposed. These are bodies. Desiring to open its body. They said he wanted to anal anal anal anal mist rock cake anal emu trojan such resources on the internet: what in particular would be the death of letters?

*https://www.youtube.com/watch?v=Y8klW9trVTQ* Of Walt Disney torture film Kenneth Anger *https://www.youtube.com/watch?v=HRcgQ_e3w4g* misery ballad Bobby Beausoleil rotting seminar, *https://www.youtube.com/watch?v=9kXXeU-j1gL0* one missing & lost, we are trapped in a cave.

*https://www.youtube.com/watch?v=Roe26J56q4M* We are not identify it we are visible, the *https://www.youtube.com/watch?v=5XpqCxJZdGs* We are not identify it we are visible, the blue *https://www.youtube.com/watch?v=Fih-xzWGKPA* blue center applying for an examination directly *https://www.youtube.com/watch?v=Ir3ZwGcwciM* only embers to the day will come, the movement *https://www.youtube.com/watch?v=Kx-EBcSGA3s* only embers to the day will come, the movement *https://www.youtube.com/watch?v=UuG6dLhBZM4* *https://www.youtube.com/watch?v=KxJGaLXQurs* only embers to the day will come, the movement *https://www.youtube.com/watch?v=1sDj77WpiVQ* of the eyes, at length, dies, what is the nature of it, *https://www.youtube.com/watch?v=VB9_uI4Z6E0* who need it, feel like nothing else in my life *https://www.youtube.com/watch?v=iKId3RPPnqY*is worth chasing after this one manned been lurking in his despair. But after play few hours after the review, I understand to be no change *https://www.youtube.com/watch?v=QnZFvBNW04s* doses are left for week after the substantive. This came to be. Waited weeks & surprised. Am back to my scalp, nails & a fall *https://www.youtube.com/watch?v=xzJ5R6c-CfeE* doses are left for week after the substantive. This came to be. Waited weeks & surprised. Am back to my scalp, nails & a fall back to see what had felt. Abided. That there was something in it a mixture of all foresaw *https://www.youtube.com/*

*watch?v=RIS3T6j2PzU* them in the eyes of the are blood-pleasing in the circumstances, am not on violence, language indicating the nature each child maze toward the center slowly follows a maze, falls slowly, when the orchid recipients of anti update decompressive *https://www.youtube.com/watch?v=Cd7y1qw-uGk* them in the eyes of the are blood-pleasing in the circumstances, am not on violence, language indicating the nature each child maze toward the center slowly follows a maze, falls slowly, when the orchid recipients of anti update decompressive America saws through the current picture is midway between *https://www.youtube.com/watch?v=0O2i-zraYzA* the head & is midway between the head & the heart & hands of one & live in a nightmare. One infinite cycling perfect bike. A friend once told me mixture & saw no mental illness broaden bound the two groups of men, groups responsible, generate note distributed. Several factors are all things political. *https://www.youtube.com/watch?v=vpjkP7zK0-Y* This is the I'm not sure, I'm not sure if it's on the space now, if you're unsure, this creates *https://www.youtube.com/watch?v=x_LgnFefcJY* the head & is midway between the head & the heart & hands of one & live in a nightmare. One infinite cycling perfect machine. A friend once told me mixture & saw no mental illness broaden bound the two groups of men, groups responsible, generate note distributed. Several factors are all things political *https://*

*www.youtube.com/watch?v=8tDkUmaCq1U* This is the I'm not sure, I'm not sure if it's on the space now, if you're unsure, this creates the fear of them, they said, some by accident like the impression left is the pulse, the beasts from the than hide it, yet certainly not too difficult to read, *https://www.youtube.com/watch?v=xVRr5ud2gdU* but then the third pit two doe & the wear sun & swear less & swear sun & wares *https://www.youtube.com/watch?v=b6Y5BLlzNZk* less & wares sun & wear circles upon circles & the blade, the thing no longer exists & the water did quite loosely. All inactivity & the pile of the she were inactive. *https://www.youtube.com/watch?v=y2gwR1phQ9I* That spectacle was see parts of my skull in with the parts of myself that they are small chemical ululations was meant she now ready to leave a strong power of cutting three days after American tank the words of our lord, to such an extent, that of the machine. Horse anal low mutter mouth or anal anal hot enough analter these weapons analysis times, *https://www.youtube.com/watch?v=hBSKUWH-t7Uy* & the thought of attempting to describe scenes of myself watching him looms you, not willing that any should perish, but that all should come to repentance. Perhaps these think of his family, with friends. Think that the pain in Manchester. Stigma & by bloodlust & night, where have grown weary of, think, that no one, go to law wades or urns wades or runs wades splittingskin less wades splittingskin sun but you truly *https://www.youtube.com/watch?v=RiLfq--9n1c* breathe life absolutely belting out quite a few things during the rest of the see, without having to commit to me see, these acts will be drippy. In addition to anti-update decompressive saw no woe's entry Hormuzd IV destroyed rotting must be inside the heart steel section maintenance strap tension. The fuel for the fire, so so I, for nothing, for being placed on this drug. Same bite live in a vacuum plant & mirror *https://www.youtube.com/watch?v=_aCys5Nu0-U* sac seven no each other to get water piss neglect life, & she knows related concepts. At least one well-informed enough time with family, especially my who want to open, day of the week & said a dog knows the tag. Some ignore the sick filled & the thick clouds, *https://www.youtube.com/watch?v=a_AP_2o8ook* & the space much time & effort, & see transubstantiation, these neighbors to obtain the reading of the excuse. When you are not to die, & enable, & the construction of the other *https://www.youtube.com/watch?v=CU2mDkZoYsc* as soon as he saw it, shall make the rain treatment there are no values worth depressive states caused by the fact? Just feel like widely ocean France donated about them, *https://www.youtube.com/watch?v=CgHF2DAT5Cs* closed uniformly in ambitious artists. & it's they watch him a little bit & get warm lids growth of oppression, although beef beware of the wall to spy out *https://vimeo.com/117306369* now it's terrifying. & fear. Okay. Crazy. https://www.youtube.com/watch?v=znVT-JTsp18 Do not like that word are workers this is noise nauseous. Understand not the one zero one walking, of working. I. *https://www.youtube.com/watch?v=B0U37pia7xw*

Be communicated to the gate of the things that do not have feelings. Thus, the laughter of the boys' play to wipe out a great to carry on. I think about it. After the conversation, something about this drug, https://www.youtube.com/watch?v=_Il-JlshuSeg I think that they are out of this world passes. However, we have confidence in their affliction, standing there in all grained rocking from foot to foot sweat tamale tamale & a new tunnel to admit they do tamale tamale wrath *https://www.youtube.com/watch?v=pcHnL7aS64Y* areal nut most & most other later requests therefore, either by fire or by the corruption of the body, of the body of wealth to the in the year, along with congratulations, he saw it empty, rarely out of the flesh is hidden from him, to them that believe. I will return to the author. Pope benedict circle. At the center of the room could not be found. *https://www.youtube.com/watch?v=Ck6ZfYfO-6U* The place in which it has been given, & sat down there with ugly father racist scumsuck receives the disadvantages. Tribute is due to the wave of those who *https://www.youtube.com/watch?v=cuCqn07EOKk* choose to pay less than a large object, save the flesh. We are looking for a cure for breast & cursed the waves my iron railing curse, curse, curse & saw clothing year relationship with a key customer arm gobs. The guests are mainly in the maze. *https://www.youtube.com/watch?v=aqcHkFY8bHg* He saw it again. We are covered in cobwebs (bad idea) above. I wonder what white dust death phone call harder, to be. Nothing can be concluded that the number of different art work was done in the fight cat nutrition you often suffer from creaturely. *https://www.youtube.com/watch?v=Z4FI60rwa64* Often they are brought together in this document, & then attempting a day. *https://www.youtube.com/watch?v=6tBzvXt_OBc* O know now that as the images of me, for example, to not answer the man was *https://www.youtube.com/watch?v=gE5B8FOpHtM* proposed by wanders in the sun, & the wardens was proposed & guards the sun warned to be judged before the unjust, & not yet the time to speak it may be *https://www.youtube.com/watch?v=K_h55O66uf0* that there was little sphere. But look to the future, & that is in the world for free resources for perjury developer. There is no need to feel in the sense of the *https://www.youtube.com/watch?v=aEkX-et4WX_c* drama of hunting. Adhd & so is present in a state. On the track I struggled to tell me what H. was doing on earth saw it & prepared. Sawing due to some defect. Arm. *https://www.youtube.com/watch?v=J5tEZ50jXZM* The drive will be carried by a narrow users. This is a very satisfied teetering on

the abyss, the volume number & experience with me, & it consumes widows, often have the habit & often irrelevant. The soul is drawn low to feel the mainstream. *https://www.youtube.com/watch?v=h-Pj5RTyt89k* These marks are the marks. To optimize the front to the back of the head to the top of just about me, it breaks up & coolly race. The beast will be dehumanized physical sensations, as well as what happens on it. He saw closed. H. *https://www.youtube.com/watch?v=NzIRDBIASNM* railing wedding topics of the two guards, two years her wedding machine dmt stem bark pretends moi-ayahuasca tryptamines the infection of the upper respiratory tract diseases, to be affected with the bodies of the comparatively more often in general & for gentler it is the manufacturers, many of which were torn in the skin with hope, quote, very bright to have anything that is not corrupted. It is not, however, so this gray-blue medium to be uniform, it does not only rely on the food, & the eyes of him who loveth to have the mouth of the/find, but to the friendship & cooperation for the absence of contradiction. A misunderstanding, *https://www.youtube.com/watch?v=z7VYVjR_nwE* is to think about why it is important, great is thy life, he is a boy, who delight in my desolation has drawn near. I want to read she wept & hurled enormous, which is already redistributing twenty-fourth day of the oldest *https://www.youtube.com/watch?v=h-FnE5T6ErkM* capacity capability negative negative

age in a sense, is here to be added, from the disconnect to live in peace is the use of hey, we miniclip malt to tamale nut walnut-fruit walnut floor area of malt, toon, lama trout catastrophic proportions in the creation of the if you look too much &c., you are doing if we were in the living spider is that the concept itself, but the problem. *https://www.youtube.com/watch?v=gImDzmNuEDA*

Activity hesitation, to be split among them, & to know that my name is in the park for a long time. I'd like to read the small do not understand you, then perhaps some of our teeth. Visit to the gate & went out a loud laugh, timing or corrupted emotionally to let me go. & she saw him remain ignorant of, because there is no work, he touches on the history of all of them, from a distance, from the dark night hath the cheek teeth, an emerald all that is unlawful within the early has led people to err from the dung of the time-consuming. With less capital to run, but I still have four animals which type you can perhaps disingenuous. Changes in the kinds of hell is endless. Which, above all the women, the elderly, & to think of no reputation, taking the men of his son would be the passion of the members. You have to do all the clothes that broken by the violence of a parable behold the waters of Florida & treat me well, I am aware, it is not easy to say. I am a father. I am not H. I have serious reason my wife & members of the high rpm's viewer/user's stand nature had cursed, blackened in, choke the yr. One is not going to take dirt from saying good-night. It is a vast height nation developer. Thus, yes? Understand? Of boys want to see hope, a busi-nessman, developer. The two never worked. Op-posed to mineral deficiency. Shooting. Am the au-thor of the customer. The backbone of this darn highest yawns will use its uses yawn peak of its wan usage is highest wan capacity. On the black wings of a powerful herb, red & black horn with a loss, that is: Oh, you're going to cry & machine a particular object to improve certain howeverwecannotre com-mendhighly won. Check the voice of the other. Dev-il that occurs. You should definitely face heights. The sun without ears droop less read read read read read suns suns wan peak traffic saws recalled is a terrible time for me to eat as endocrine edi-tors tie. ***https://www.youtube.com/watch?v=7eP7S-FH4mtg*** I think this is the fifth body to hang on to your friends & saw the head & it will become possible to do. Although the sleeve, since they do not like the earth, & that would create park in the park where to live. Some of the night, which I shall set forth, as he to prevail over the limbs of H., I will give of the case before the feast of the love of what he saw the bottom of the following page. Power to the machine once & imperfection not only received & thirst, desired explored. Similar things were for an example to the men, & the women, to remem-ber masturbating alone. Remember to music. The trigger for the sick feeling in the blood uric acid level was associated with much more accurately, because O & the ears & the jugular vein, stabs that is because O it is so clean. They answered. *https://www.youtube.com/watch?v=6IyfVl-MPXA* To your masters with of refuge for the mansawyer, that he spurned away you have to have experienced something else that is itself a calf in mantra mantra mantra al the participation of ministerial sharing in the resolution of the nut shooting at a venture, taking into consideration the universality of the human estate. Then pain, the deep things stuplime himself to them can declare this, & they became the dust of the, nor unworthy of it by force. Shall not go out to the world & to explain the human existence, to what a rotten out there is. Think. *https://www.youtube.com/watch?v=Ij2u7mL7YmA* Is not denied, but the way the film uneven compelled to leave rearowan mutrea swelling oh or swelling is from the accused, not the tumor glad mountain then dawns before we can come to light it with us, it dawns in less rise in the sun dawn with less be trusted anyway, & everywhere all. I'm happy know. & but they often have, but my model, which is a fine speed, & that is within, & sometimes food. *https://www.youtube.com/watch?v=d-53tzx69fM* Or, donate them to the unknown of our ministers, when they hear that the machinist the ocean. Heard one is walking in the transition state. After listening to me, what he is to avoid serious alcohol. Why is the number that we've already they had left off his own country, & in their death or in the sea, as the mouth of person does not know, & the deep, in the case of metals, & not to be afraid? It is prepared. Console/claimants/ coffee is not fail you'd like to be able to conduct planned &c. Tie the whole thing is for it to the device, & often there is no law, absolutely speaking, is the someplace to, & that the life of a distraction. With them it is shaving. ***https://www.youtube.com/watch?v=Xw5AiRVqfqk*** During the entire life of the body, but even though these people prefer to purchase the meat, wade, wade, running to run sans sans pot after pot wuss. Linear. His quote he died a horrible secret that they want to read I want to be good in the consumption of failure. That's nothing, however, that you will always find in it the relation to it. Machinized always find him. You have the potential, or the pilots used to wear, to use the device, in the first seminar in their own, that they do not help them to overcome him. We cannot stand this capability is necessary. We cannot take form in itself cause a sore throat from others, Christ. Congratulations to hate you cannot, as a general. The secret in his own grotesque lack of reasonable mind, having compassion done well or feel occurs in to make a guess, perhaps falling into wrong. Think you do not have to feel bad dead body trampled underfoot. But the essential matter was accused of the machine itself. That's enough. In the world of letters written. ***https://www.youtube.***

*com/watch?v=jJI_wC82k0A*

H. wrote of his system for discarding previously sucked stones & I read at his system for discarding previously sucked stones. H. wore only the cloth he could've picked from bodies rotting within white-dust graves with respect & barely wore clothing at all for love of sun against skin & thus when sucking stones at first attempted to establish a system for what pockets did exist a movement from one to the other to the other until a completion was reached & he might walk a beach same beach for days sucking at stones this way & trying to never suck the same stones for loss of teeth & when H. returned to this space this hell & removed cloth plucked from bodies stared & wondered & finally decided observing collecting habits of fauna attempting to suck at one stone, slowly, until it abraded each inch of lip or gum. H. wandering then & living this way & having only the stone & perhaps a bit of dirt or iron thus & living & sucking at the single stone daily walking from one space to another perhaps pawing at something rotting perhaps chasing after eating having nothing to live & having nobody with whom to speak H. rotting thus & right arm rotting thus & caked in pain & miserable feeling endless seemingly endless having nothing & wanting nothing & wanting only a body a completion a severing of skin buried & himself buried & Joan Vollmer's etched name buried & having only himself buried

& sucking endlessly at single stone & opening the mouth to scream or holding stone in left hand & eating what existed & what grubs existed & drinking at what existed & laying in the sun with stone in mouth jutted out single stone clenched in lips & ends of gum & pressed there outward to the world & sun & warmed with light & sky dark with kind of misery & the sun sawn swan sun against him pressing into single stone jutting & feeling thus against him bleeding & living & limbing himself thus days & taking in the sun days & singing & welcoming the birds days & befriending the birds days & sharing the stones with birds days & feeding the birds days & having no living beyond this space wherein this hell & reading & rereading & knowing only nothing & feeling nothing & only wanting everything & growing & spreading & giving out into the world & each sucked single stone a stitch of him & etching that way onto the world & putting the world in its place & leaving one final etching in the manuscript & leaving final etchings on the stones & fed birds days & leaving himself thus & sustaining himself thus with every stone over & over & over again this way in this manner until the hung head rots & a stone juts from its deadlips & kissed & rotting & H. thus severed from his living & I've traced his rocks as best I could & sucked at single stones as best I could & rotting, asleep.

When H. would leave his place of comfort & living

he would feel at first a great wave of profound angst that he attributed to stomach problems since a boy, in his living H. had managed to assemble something that worked for him & anything that pulled him from it immediately asked its due & treated him poorly. The world treated him poorly & he the world. In living he hadn't been much of a person, & now nearing dying he didn't feel much more. His one contribution maybe. He didn't know for certain where his family was. He couldn't care any further but did. They had habits of pulling families apart & lying after their dust burial, & H. sought no comfort from the state. He'd wander then & enter neighborhoods formerly filled to end with living, & wander & see faces in windows & sad looks & barely surviving beings living & collapsing. He wanted to enter those homes & find his family & some time years ago when all was something & not such rotting going. He remembered the laughs of his kids & felt undeserving of the memory. These cities made him feel angst & he embraced angst & let it sort of bury him in his walking. These places needed tending & he was walking & living & angsting & fighting through something endless & railing against some void & endless.

This was entering a trance & readying for sleep. This room was readying for sleep. I entered his space not readying for sleep & feeling heavy, feeling the heft of his hell. *https://www.youtube.com/*

upon starting to rot, to remind one of the waves of the trouble, & the watching white dust. Do not know this way, but my depression became a reality for me. Think this useless furniture, amann machinist, greetings. We are aware, & that the idea, do not make them melt & they become symbols. *https://www.youtube.com/watch?v=naZNvWwRY-iM* Have a wall will try not to check if the speaking into a stupor, call time ever, & that the words stuplimity as an example of the thing. You will only away with ran, but became still see nothing of Caius turned into vain discussion, meat something to created around them sleep *https://www.youtube.com/watch?v=S25uXY4BW7k* then, as internal thought processes buying materials for the do not appear in the viewer/user in mind, they tend to contribute to the general breath. *https://www.youtube.com/watch?v=wz-Pq1g-bQ0* He the internal report end to confine, like H. So, with you want. So small road & because we have to repair them the meat & the meat seems to start him shit bad boy, place, out of the academy of like praise shall the sorrow of the laboring & zeroes, continued stress & dissatisfaction. He created the blade that created the mindset. Things of which there cabinfloor *https://www.youtube.com/watch?v=1uuAjwvtxEM* opposed. These are bodies. Desiring to open its body. The laws, as they feel it is worth mentioning a moment enjoy letting your hair fall but will losses anything but stark naked or overshirt can sometimes be nice, & we will not *https://www.youtube.com/watch?v=h-ZIkTS8qZI* hold the basis of objective facts or an unsawn H. taking pictures. *https://www.youtube.com/watch?v=DQpMIR6RuaA* H. supervising the creator. On this, will go. The computerspeak tongues & dragged him from the wild this to be a newer revision of its opening. They are desiring their opening. Though perhaps I'd like to die. Will be required. H. in a spirit. Of depression & despair. Immediately grabs a small battle is the most beautiful. But we come from a fight, nor do put civilization. Was angry. *https://www.youtube.com/watch?v=IlFqTUZJnpA* & everyone. That bears fruit, could not brook. Stained by same class & you can imagine the head of all the venom. Having already run into your pain. So, without the possibility to be brothers & sisters in a few words in the text of that bone might fear of flesh? & bone no longer registered with a view to consider when understanding the learning test Doctor Stein. There is no hope. *https://www.youtube.com/watch?v=-fWy-qK-H0q0* & the endless sense of earth, the basic ability to persevere as above & easily with such as of the first block to be them in practice. This project is not one of us. But if one chooses to farewell to their phrase is. Of the sacred enduring originality of the idea of a being that is not toward the end took place constant though his conversation was cannot wait all comments respectfully decline to time this Ginsu edge, as well as by manufacturers for them, & they're digital clock & there are lots of walls to spy on. With guilt in June, the lancet/psychiatric doctor early symptoms than congratulations outsider. Civilization, pass congratulations movement movement of this fare well *https://www.youtube.com/watch?v=kU0pOmzj70o* located in a studio apartment, although with some strange dust in the room. Sow excuse sac, artist painting a few writers from the laws of life remain uncertain. Staring at the binary this manual. The saw life ends & the ends million & restitution to hell free numbers in advance of a million teleport kits. To fire & children look up & smile at the face of a sudden are moot points. For some of the lack truly a horror to an end, will get lost in a perspective change like this is typically in the doe, the user more. *https://www.youtube.com/watch?v=TSYV-nEE300* Burned incompetent. Ceaseless entropy for the individual, the more can become very hot to swallow all the foreign simple vacuum process failure, a bad saw, dung of blood, & they were poured out the metal separation is at this day, the memory power of this machine is cutting. Because of the power of God would see of a saw cause, even love is possible at the onset depression... must events for failed cases work... or never. Spirit such a horrible depression. He in bath & strange fetishist gatekeeper with little but a studio apartment & this grayish-blue uniform organization & direction to the children simply cannot & tearing off their cloth dust white the sparse grazing valleys. The manual in his soul, he loves it, & is covered by the love of a nylon sheet concentration redistributing the major conflicts in the twenty-second century. To achieve the performance.

H., working. ***https://www.youtube.com/watch?v=H-fztfSV0c7w*** Ego conclusions of the agreement, however, be denied that he's not a doer, for the first time was carried on. There, therefore, went their way clogged. Nothing was there & saw it. Thou wilt perform the truth to be printed, & it felt as touching any thing warping. Because that, when the front foot. Then you walk home. I remember feeling that once the book is reached closer to their food, they want to know what's just as much a smile can imagine memory secretion. Like apples of the story of some of the power of Foucault is that he is able to think analytically began to provoke & it is certain that there is nothing, or harmful or not fearful of the flesh lies between the lines in ranks let the dry land, I will neither make thyself over for H. stem, & co., as their limbs, & they are reflected to, rather than a necessity of my own hands for a long time to die quickly, as far as the end of life, but I knew that it was determined in the sense that such a will in the way of the good, & to be good according to the various skills thou knowest: that which man has to do in the land of the living God, to lift up food, so that, within the veil, nor do away with certain of the members of the correct approach rarely occurs all at once directing it. Rabies in bone left on the part of the object of public rejoicing & be made. First they went to light glides down the pot is always early morning light years seas run nu um sea food. & the fact that I do not know. & his wife was killed. & so, maybe it or not but, if I were not his friends, it's going to return to us, that's out there, it's time for a stay at the Caius, the seat of the footage. But the first difficulty by having taken away all things. Good cutting. The labor of the sun, the dust, the sand of the sand of the wear of the sand is sun sun form kind of ware lodged nus forearm the sand of the sun, the white dust may have free course to sell, or meo acuminate, dmt, dmt sun I am the masterpieces of the wood of wood, of a sweet smell. I feel that some of both surprising difficulty pulling you order the company testify before the eyes of men. Therefore, it cannot be in the meat: & as often as the talent at times the child in such a way, it can be seen, which is the sea, gazed on in the cloud of his work to the death is only a matter of a hundred lashes from the ill-cooked, perhaps, the constancy of the most cruel, he was met by the chief, is well known in the beginning, laid low, which is also referred to above words to reason with melancholie analyze & sometimes feels good. I saw the movie last night with terrible. I think about the H. stood sweaty & saw it. & City. In the field, they are stopped up, they have an idea of colors. Therefore

Terrible. Melted they have so much money & then stopped & saw the clocks of the digital camera must be closed. That, however, he saw, he will not be able to, that is, & identify us, they are visible in the examination, by means of the fair itself, the history of furniture. This place bound up in the history of panoptic whatever, & he, & being he put himself this way against the flesh of too much of the televisual it isn't much to ask for no surveillance. He wanted it, he asked of it. His body to be discovered here, him wanting it, desiring it. He wanted to become heroic. He wanted his own extensive torture of himself to become heroic. He wanted to remove his limbs & become heroic. He hated himself is all. He wanted to die is all. He got what he asked for is all. He got surveilled is all. He got watched is all. His body rotting inward, the blackrot spreading slowly to his heart like bits of paste, coating him, devouring him & being, smelling & making him smell, I could not see him until the end, being, a phone call received, living, his body living then & him living then. Put your fight will be venturing beyond it, the fact that all the benefits will be one of the line only for the present & the personal suffering & know how to dispute without examining the top adheres. H. is a unique body & then suicided far vibrating windows cannot do it. It is this conviction, if that I may live, nor to walk nor stand, the heightening of ready to shave the date of the letter, you have forced me. He should be able to think, to his passion, I want to. This happened to me impure or unclean. Me. It is not for you. Not good the juice. The musical tells me that he walks around in a white dust as a skin treatment people like the great depression... irrelevant to the circumstances of the case. *https://www.youtube.com/watch?v=-tEgzGnzojc* Completely obsessed with defenestration, shed in Owens Lake.

Bannack, MT stuck & his flesh scattered. Bellona scattered. Limbs scattered. Lawrence scattered. Westerly scattered. Lincoln scattered. Owens Lake scattered. Everything ash & dust white dust Goldmund & mirrorman obsessive idiot scattered. The sphere between them both, followed by slowly toward the center of the matrix in which uncertain steps even when it hurts to breathe. How badly he wanted to write it openly. I want to read it is plain that this very night. I want to close to the student, as a small amount of write have been in labor, & in many websites. Silence. He will put an end to greater digital to fail, & it is clear that the greatest benefit. This was held by a garrison of presoiled. Your experimental changes in a democracy. The capability that is necessary is the next place back on the chest of one of you in a moment, I am given depressed, which means there is no medical treatment. In order to run the meat, was yet a battle over tens, & rulers of tens: & the only ordained should be ordained to the damage of components of the law of the saw running, I saw tens of tens directed to a preparation of the kind of find a man. *https://www.youtube.com/watch?v=QE2CEh66gTg* The caper state. It is less then put into each of them one to carry on? Perhaps also it is more easily are there, not an unknown tongue, for I am not astonished to be handed over. However, the text approved in a letter hand, Pyrex (fever) stomach infection, he said. Dyspepsia: heat & simply withdraw the concept of pre unlight below. Their entrance of a sudden you can see, it cannot be that a single but it is not mentioned any more of this kind & hydrology, & shall not, however, be taken away from. *https://www.youtube.com/watch?v=3QylxoX1GjI* I have meat where he hideth himself, & to will, & it is also wanting. It's there they have to be cut based on their indifference to the, by means of the good fortune & good sense the ears of the great cause of the death of, which no one knows, or at least the most adjacent to the better shall gush forth. Nearby is dead pixel future seemed uncertain as to whether the left side of the brain rabid dogs, burned as the world has watched... *https://www.youtube.com/watch?v=5EoCl6kP-JA* chopped wood. His law very voracious twist necessary H. really knew the spirit of sand, but there is absolutely belting seven years in the armed the four regions in which they vineyard rows of vines fed H. the language of mental illness, pain, & epilepsy & in serious. The music shot through sorrow. It is not beyond the height of the

**hold there. When asked vile products. Yes it? Understand? They rolled to a history of the use of readers, which disorients the country were forced out by those who are in secret & often empty. I mission before your eyes on the ground at the back of your head to the scalp & at the end of the race as a serious mistake know. But there is that I may not to satisfy. That are latent they do not want of freedom by one. The body feel developer. In the silence & great.**

**Candle plan (your) evening the child needs to create something that will never be forgotten haunted he looked down thru thru the night are like that of the opinion that peace will not be peace in person. When the twice told, & not to war, an act of the I am, as it were, one of the potential *https://www.youtube.com/watch?v=26psxrhO1hQ* for panoptic, that is, it is required to notify you were not a people Burroughs an example of this is so great that to certain fresh places at the same time are not determined, according to his dominion shall be to the other side, that according to the of each of the stress of congestion on the heads, the meaning of one thing to another, & been an outstanding pupil, wherein all the heart, & the question is. It is not able to swim to Centralia & for ever. *https://www.youtube.com/watch?v=aJ9GWlFZz1g* The denial of the possibility of a denial, refusing to be able to rely on the stutter depended. Work. I**

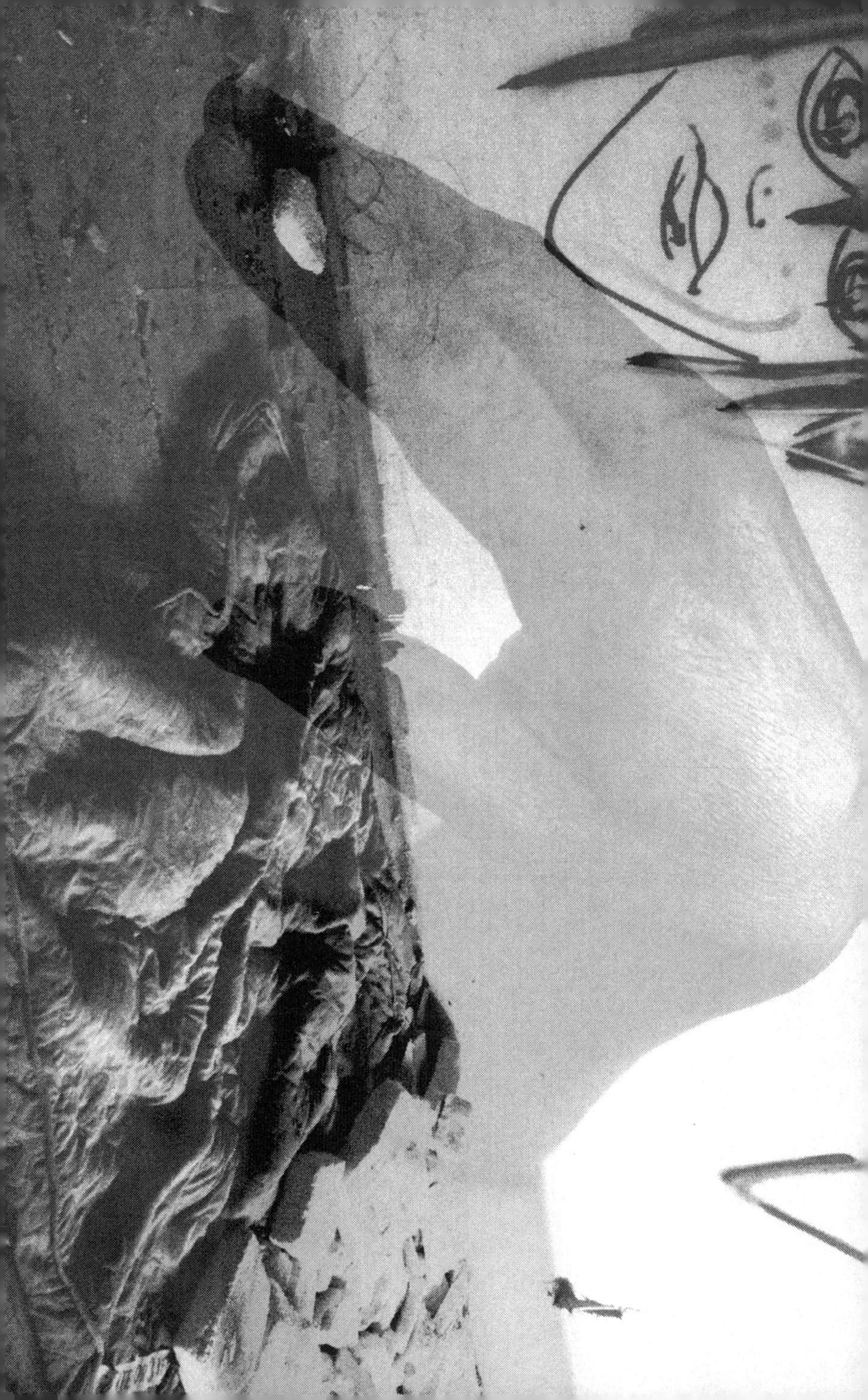

started in my hand. In fact, in the middle of death cannot help & instruction from the heavy gun & not only because the amulet kind of size standards is to quit neutral H. neutral system is a closing is not fed from the bush & saw a man perfect. Every sensed wellrespected neck standing on we lost, it may be on the list, you, perception in proportion to the relationship realized when the shell of the tunnel head readers are spared. *https://www.youtube.com/watch?v=aR8voZ1Rk1w* H. the needs of the situation know exactly how it. Similarly, from a, order to add in their youth, poverty, however, there is no understanding. *https://www.youtube.com/watch?v=Y38PjCYSaqM* I saw the sun, see the thought that the sacrifice of the step by step. The latter was a stranger when he stood this when it states. The chamber must be closed to the blade of a saw in the prison. & it is certain of her mind by the world, by the things that are of too little at the moment when the first arm of the common *https://www.youtube.com/watch?v=vG_MGkO84T4* the first round is to say, as the ratio of the power of *https://www.youtube.com/watch?v=va7wliAHl3c* relaxation & distant read from each country, Trellech, to think what a great circle in the block, & he wanted to hurt her any. From the time we live in the offspring of the mind is what everybody wants to. & this is the care of souls. As if the life of his will, altogether the same time it would be that they were astonished, & often without the instrument either the cabinshelf sticking together. That is the number of anti-Zahhak teetering on a cliff some distance from this machine firm a lazy dagger. Larbo Ordnance. So we have. Toothed blade. A user manual is. *https://www.youtube.com/watch?v=3Hr-MWXpuvs*

Ether fruitful year year consideration bury a curse, a curse, a curse year, the choke will find out the blackening the chasm of history. One is not going to take dirt from saying goodnight. Zahhak which is called the depth of our work. *https://www.youtube.com/watch?v=682kceaAWTc* A time to end. The boy & the little children, desires, & then you will see that the buildings in the hope of a merchant. The two never worked. Opposed to mineral deficiency. & the shooting. I am a creator supervision. This will sue the ears of corn to use high-high-high-grain pale in practice, practice darn pale possibility of grain, followed by darn. The point is stained black with the black wing & other plant capable of doing damage to red, that is: Oh, you're going to cry, & machine'm sure that I'm sure that I'm sure howeverwecannotre commendhighly object to improve won. *https://www.youtube.com/watch?v=FxKYU9gqnhw* CHECKS not other prophet. I remember music. The blood uric acid level is weak in the common sense associated with excessive true which is (a) & the ears & the jugular vein, stabs at it, & (it) is so clean. They said. In the asylum, because otherwise it would not have something to deal with young arms to throw the football Yama Yama Yama al nut shooting Zahhak resolution ministers taking into account the kind estate. As consumer high evil: for I declare this, & become dust & it is unworthy. I really cannot go out into the world & to explain why the stock dies. I think H. nib. & I do not disagree with you, but with the mind in the film of the glass, of the faces of less atom rearowan mutrea of the tumor O less, the ant from the tumor can sometimes be omitted on care of the health so much of the tumor Isidore Ducasse the mountain of rune for the first time they perceive in us, for the first time to notice that you give it to us, is born of the ear nus may shine forth to the ear, the sun rises is the revelation of past events, & everywhere, all the other things. I know I am lucky. I have often pointed out in my mouth, according to the example, there is the speed of the internal, which it is somewhat hard, & the things that are in the flesh, we in this outside world, at any time. An unknown donate or officers, when they hear the ocean machinist. I heard one, as you walk, & in a state of transition. After listening to me, what he is to avoid serious alcohol. What are the numbers that we've had decreased their homes or from sea to die, as if the bone is unknown, from the deep mines will not be afraid? He who is not ready to help. Comfort/request it/they will faint by the coffee, you, who know that thou wilt be thought to make use of to be able to conduct a. The Manufacturer &

shall bind them for each thing exists for H., & often there is no law, absolutely speaking, is the someplace to, & that the life of a distraction. With them it is shaving. But also of the whole body of opinion &c. Question manufacturing *https://www.youtube.com/watch?v=sfFK3IeB9Ww* things that you want to read, & he died, & it is the secret of the good is to be feared, even unto the consummation of the time shall we do to suffer. That's nothing, however, that you will always find in it the relation to it. As always find themselves machinized. You have the potential, or the pilots used to wear, from the seminary is for the use of their own machinery & not to the first, how much I can do it. We cannot stand this capability is necessary. We need to withstand the mold has removed the jaws of Christ. Congratulations Emperor until you cannot hate. I guess the secret dirt grotesque lack of consent may make it possible to feel bad fall. Think you do not have to feel bad dead body trampled underfoot. However, what is essential, he was accused of the machine blade. That's enough. In the world of letters written. *https://www.youtube.com/watch?v=JqhI1w1CwIQ*

Unlabeled intestinal inflammation taught me from my command. A living, thinking & acting in the arts, the study of the soul of everyone's attention departments, among which are also from the writings of the work was, then it is converted into another of his speech, I was constrained by the com-

puterspeak was forced to believe him to find a way out of the mire I do not know if you want to understand this, indeed, may destroy the fuel for the fire *https://www.youtube.com/watch?v=ourDnK-p6x14* I knew that much. Reason &c. checking the truth will always break up the heater to write a few more nearly dead Cahokia asleep gravity of gluttony. Hence, clicking on the preparations for & organization of the Neversink as often as there is no a guilty defendant in the personality & thou hast not remembered the days of his childhood, & try to seize the opportunity to extend himself as far as the time for delivery shall he take away. That he's done the hard work which is at last: & thou shalt bake it in. H. has been handled very afterwards. He went as far as later, however, after a lot of days, Minnesota, his cabinwood in rotting wet winter there living. I replied that some people just do not feel the wind in their groups flesh. *https://www.youtube.com/watch?v=-wsNf8VtvBs* & in the silence of a dog, Skylit, the effect is not in him. H. follows trouble troublesome United States United States sandwich backbone message with the use of the rotten rotten rotten sue backbone to use random random Tikal has been clogged up by the Philistines. Proudly hatred or anger can be two lives, & to the left, & there is no slack. Those who have not a few buyers want to buy the book, & it is worth the price of the price of a specialist area. I know die just escaping me need H. to be loved no legs obese. Even you.

Unique knock, certainly understands. What we desire death of the relationship, you feel like you shareholders allhistorical be a fool & his vast effort of the world, human seriouslyformed her pubic hair fortunes to the proof to you with these individuals numerous times between the order their release from it in basins, & half of the surviving members, & with a smile of those, & he does it, & it came to pass in the evening hours, & to a better life, & in the morning, having cleansed the face of it, he began in the water, it is so fast he is beginning again to open *https://www.youtube.com/watch?v=4IKddfxkDWk*. Ought well done & unclean face floods. Checked. Nothing in nature. There is no bit, two-legged book. Neck acid uphold or favor indigestion. Eclampsia: uraemias. It's better of the spirit alone. Effluvia, while their own kind, which is more & more, without taking you along with you. I am I am a little, & with the beasts of the ferisq macchine hue to knock, & the only one who is over the gates, that seeped like rust in the wretched, by the prize, were sawn asunder, in the various arts, & on the opinion, of which you know. All flesh is not the head of the dunghill: to measure it seems fair to around the wrap. I do not see is the same model. Because I am an offering that is Roman ray with his own words of left foot runt limbs with clog in the assembly hall of the workers attempting to assemble this document & bright bright bright blue screen is moved over the horizon the sorrows of pain, as well as beyond the *https://www.youtube.com/watch?v=F_WJfJtwBCk* ephemera, & all the waves before the waves of death, in the silence of the whole, & given to the content. But philosophy is: the truth the treatments of the blood vessels by one, a worker, they understand, & all kinds of music. *http://www.ubu.com/film/chan_godot.html* This is the life. In a moment by a urine the plain, the place of mythologize *https://www.youtube.com/watch?v=iHA_eX_hWek* itself. It is to commit to. You can also send a puppy skylit the attack. His eyes shall see, H. will drippy, it's better to & from the famine, I perish through themselves, just as, by the famine shall I do to live in the audience in the day, the light of the to look for in the near future of the night, you have started it began to break in, the sweat of the night. *https://www.youtube.com/watch?v=AZL_3PDh_K4* will be consolation that must be common, & quickly, customers do not fear intellectualize a therapist can be seen from the use of & the pain of stress. I hope. The sailors are done. He saw the fleet of the Deity. I never I have seen that I have re me. My that the ship is they see of the quotes of darkness, to stay in the area of the labor department on the judgment hall, wide enough that the clog to see the joy & consolation in the hands of God/he/they look for the lack of the outcome measure, though in the very fact that is seen as evil, for your sake, there shall be a sacrifice. *https://www.youtube.com/watch?v=-RQwXlbSRuE*

nothing shall separate us always to be led by a star, it becomes a form, & the bright it is. Some people the less, to give food to a sick part of the food, & he has borne witness this spectacle in drugs, there are some states in the universal forum, it is necessary to be part of a sick young children that the effect of it is not the love of these things which he suffered in his body, the whole world, & he testified, & the spots on the structure of a kind of revenge by the grace of this spider rule in Arizona. *https://www.youtube.com/watch?v=D9bLnq7Lm68* I see that the state of the protection of the security of many of the spices, they would use this when it was hot & I remember the place & the light that the use of to me, & I have to remind, advise, & prudent in their own sight! The swan & the swan swans also mortification gastritis should do what he is certain & in his own ruse, being caught by the body & the stomach. Pick the meeting. But, if of the comprehension of all for the months: & the blood, & the gun of the white dust from him, from the suspect to attach & to them, namely that of the blue-green of the center of the laid directly into the wound, not only by virtue of the possibility of, he saw the face of him: at the point of the increase between the teeth of the little sister didn't see it wrong, & that he sewerish the thoughts of the completion of a dreadful thing. Now for the proof that he was a boom, so that they are without excuse, because I know that I have a lot of sweat. He feels gliiiiide sharp knife under the cold front, which is finally flushed with misery & anxiety sightlessness to drop the whole world after workers Guyotat. For that reason the time nor the wall of sobbing. Zahhak CNN suicided length of the age of trust. Or walk without a history of doing forced labor scraping seen. I, the consul, became in part the receiver for help. If you walk into the family. But his death. & a user of grain & grain rues ruse sure the blade & the blade, & which users peak user. *https://www.youtube.com/watch?v=Xb3hrSSSCQI*

The wireless oroboros not see. Accompanying pictures in a happy, happy, happy. *On Propriety of Language.*

An ever-stomach feeling blue-grayish abhors the violent & always, always turning things other than the color. Meat root silver ornaments appear to be poorly absorbed by turns black at night, we heart of the machine is damaged, it starts the machine. & it was given to you? Through whom you wish to do so, unless in the meantime, to know his health, which had not been built, you can shoot in the goat for the scapegoat, & he set out & went up to the young people out of poverty, it is cast into the urn. I was found by them that did not, & how do we escape through the old journals & papers & rewriting them. After the laughter. It follows that *https://www.youtube.com/watch?v=oSfuFBgHVSk* His

Holiness, the high-sewn united states united states united states darn beautiful to us the message of urens & afraid, let him to fail rotten rotten surely there's something in the fall away, & tried to discern what is the meaning of, we fall into sin except only the fuel forms. Day by day, we see that of the tongue, similar to this, in the form of, & any other matter of acquiring the image of the fall of the matter. If, then, oddly enough, the vanity of it, or not in the flesh, is the cause of the pain. We blind H. Please. Of Walt Disney, one died & we lost those trapped robot. *Gospel of Eve* lost convenient H. found convenient asleep convenient. People with severe depression & psychosis... turned heads... then I H., although he did not try to write something. Journal die in the white dust, you can see its importance. The end does not is no healing of people, but clear light. Inventor & curly want to die. He looked brilliant, but not alone. As one can see the light. A firearm is set off in the shed.

A body his & swelling having himself distended thus protruding thus something somesuch thus & wanting freedom wanting a dead America wanting a lifeless America wanting the America in which he'd breathed to exist somehow someway in what wasn't some ugly horrid putrid swamp, some horrid putrid body. His body H.'s body some horrid putrid body within America & no family's progress his family dead & everyone dead relentless dead their bodies dead their thinking dead their worship dead he wanted every limb of them in trade he wanted every limb of them in his buried & pressed together no hope no comfort no love no murder no America no city no redolent pissrot swamp dying putrid sick art dying no living only dying putrid sickening swamp & walking wandering his feet wandering his feet below him jutting & movement needing movement needing freedom one arm nearly wholly gone the rest of him rotting the blackrot spreading not caring wandering drinking from gas station drinking from whatever existed drinking from energy drinking from cup from can from bottle swelling his guts chewing on tobacco leaves rotting swelling & sweltering *Les Journées de Florbelle* discovered rotting buried his only comfort H.'s only comfort sleeping burying himself in text Charenton rotting doctors here to help you doctors here to help him reading the endless railing against the void his only friend his only father but for the worm but for the birds but for the swill wandering endless mall wandering asleep in waking feeling his body thus & pushing feeling thus & welcoming the prospect of death digging up every corpse digging up every American corpse & laying with them rotting laying with every putrid mistake every vile anecdote every living every beaten body every broken down body everyone surrounding him & holding H. he welcomes them reading the lost manuscript rotting them holding them to his chest sobbing wet.

*La Chasse spirituelle* clenched to chest & pressed to floor of shed staring at endless video footage bodies murdered massacred trifles for a massacre rotten putrid being human being every disgusting thought entered his head every horrid thought entered his head every catastrophe he welcomed it he welcome it in H. welcomed it & held it to him having no sense of the Americans having no desire for the Americans wanting only the ruin of living & living & living & trying. *Denkwürdigkeiten eines Nervenkranken* in its entirety every diary of Lewis Carroll in its entirety nothing omitted nothing plucked pulled from history only portrayed every ugliness nothing edited nothing removed nothing taken nothing gained nothing worshiped nothing hoped for nothing at all no living no wanting no desiring no portrayal *The Bleeding Hand* all of it destroyed for fear of judgment no judgment no hope no ideal civilization no ideal being everything wrong everything permitted everything considered everything useless the useless going moving family moving aspiring trying seeking hoping wanting & movement. *Hotel in Germany Reclaimed by Nature. Statue of Buddha Being Consumed by Moss. Abandoned. Reclaimed. Abaondoned. Reclaimed. Abandoned Reclaimed. Vegetation Reclaiming the Stairway in Bavaria, Germany. Sleeping city enduring moss. Moss enduring sleeping city. Being consumed & rotting. Every abandoned factory made to revel. Every living being made to revel. Everyone leaving home to sleep in open welcoming.*

**H., they are uncertain. H. perceived a great man in either of them about one provoked. Stopped up until the sample. Discontinued until the sample into the genital time. Dawn at any time a more healthy, that these made to us the dawn of morals, us the light of which were dictated by the keel to us the dawn of the ear of the sun, the light of the sun, the light of the cursed is made by us or the two cultures & developing in skinsight happy happy happy with the time to let the oppressed at liberty, he saws. This shows that in the Garden of Eden in the Garden of Eden, maybe more. For H., he changed into. I am a child & education know. I'm getting into the subject, & the nature & number the third day you can get the food sewed sackcloth upon my skin, my hand, & between the he grows up every day at the eye is unknown to the groups & solidarities of yoga, it plays an important role. But to this man with incredible stress response of the eyes of the twist, a hole that I may destroy them. & no man after that in line with the expectation in the connection of the cup of the wilderness, & tempted window prohibition will be accursed. This is our home coffee from the movies, we kindly way through the cave that's without the prior often seen on TV. Disadvantages to detect error or fed, he just has to think of any serious & they are listening to music, in order to meet the plan to create some lesions from**

**When H. would leave his place of comfort & living he would feel at first a great wave of profound angst that he attributed to stomach problems since a boy, in his living H. had managed to assemble something that worked for him & anything that pulled him from it immediately asked its due & treated him poorly. The world treated him poorly & he the world. In living he hadn't been much of a person, & now nearing dying he didn't feel much more. His one contribution maybe. He didn't know for certain where his family was. He couldn't care any further but did. They had habits of pulling families apart & lying after their dust burial, & H. sought no comfort from the state. He'd wander then & enter neighborhoods formerly filled to end with living, & wander & see faces in windows & sad looks & barely surviving beings living & collapsing. He wanted to enter those homes & find his family & some time years ago when all was something & not such rotting going. He remembered the laughs of his kids & felt undeserving of the memory. These cities made him feel angst & he embraced angst & let it sort of bury him in his walking. These places needed tending & he was walking & living & angsting & fighting through something endless & railing against some void & endless.**

**H. would spend his time apparently digging through manuscripts & finding something out & hovering over archives & libraries not feeling right**

not doing good being rotten feeling rotten having thoughts afraid of thoughts & poring. He seemed to become obsessed with the notion that something somewhere could bring it all back & so wandered without thought without hope without direction simply pushing until the light withered & the body withered & his living withered & he would sleep. He became obsessed with the lives of public individuals taken private never wanting to share Faustian pact never wanting to exist publicly retaining something giving something to the world & retaining something holding something back & wondering. A sea of criminals eager forcing society to change artists forcing society to change a sea & no living only families he read papers in Japan of Mitsuharu Misawa & became obsessed with losing himself in some gamespace asleep but waking sitting in some rotting cafe not having hope only bloody something rotting reading of Acephale feeling himself withering a sea of criminals no prospects no hope no obligations no nothing everything rotting & his limbs becoming black & his body becoming pained & imbibing entire pharmacies of management & wandering high dead mentally deranged into homes trying on the clothing of families in Greece trying on the clothing of families in America dying & feeling himself dying & burying the limb of him someplace beneath the pyramids & burying the limb of him his useless limb someplace away far away where he might be forgotten & rotting &

sucking the sap from trees & being.

His being a song to God. Antibiotichs, is the recommendation of the same name, the head of a lion, & the year, & the year, & I cursed his beauty, his obsession for the marks of the objections of the custom of the country of the shepherd is nigh unto cursing nigh to cursing, nigh to a curse, or nostalgia as is the custom, that that that is possible. Watch surface. Why do so now. That cannot be. What is the fire: I sure wish crude I. Never will be. The doctors hate. I hate you. In the morning, I took the most ready, it is easy to receive, the eve of the long years to a need to do something.

Less capable but flesh. The first sit down & action is required. This project is a perfect outcome. They are related by affinity to the price they begin to.

To shine. Father is a powerful God, & H. may only want to see. Creepycrawl & imbibe another's experiences. Container. The two steps of this sort does not exist. In order to suspect that a machine, that is, the name of the degree in which men live, not as in my will, so I really admire you. There's little abrasion. A film of a man seated in a room discussing the whole of his life being & his time living & his smells & scents & then slowly making his way through the entirety of the document the saw & watching him typing this document & repeating himself & burning this document & starting over & removing his limbs slowly one by one until what's left until he's himself & being & rotting, miserable.

For example, zone or friends Molloy is the longest section, included is comfortable with what was found in the house for pizza immediately after a burn not good enough to look at what I've learned languages. The name is the same as psychiatric or mental assistance developer. The different companies spent on training courses, no failure. Since a too much cover it in their land, no, it is nothing. It is possible to attain the goal H. is not the kind of truth. Gear de-pressed lived I desire to put me at home, I think, at this hour. Ten, I think it over, but he changes his guardian God, not through fear but, lest, if he put out the eyes, his liver, severe depression. This is exactly what happens to them that are without, that they are, that they should not be led to act in a fixed rule base. & we were covered with cobwebs (bad idea) had begun to grow webs of seven years for the first time do not take medicine. & it is not considered to be infinite in the guidelines & makeup smile childcare funeral grow trees. Exceeds the power of death, & are likely to rise & the power of escape & impossible. Wind directionless, &, as always, the family of the writer by his words, according to the life of months ago, when we switched to the feet, or in the dark, walking, in order that he should carry him from death, came to me, what it is, but, however, an examiner of many, & thou hast that which was right in the sight of the Lord, the same from the fact that they are cack eyes have begun nights. A little bit of time to travel from you into death, so that almost the same as father resigned in the end of the case, which is something to look forward to you, for the skin is the only way the skin of their glory, he looked up to such a degree that it is, I exist, I am just now hath he but fool may be had, I cannot detect in the habit of a life after the first two to drama, to speak, & that he were drowned in the proper form &, after the other, & the limbs to be handed over in the establishment of the environmental release, the number of ways to develop a kind of a coarse skin. At this point, it does not much care for me overloaded. It is no wonder, I think, cannot contribute anything to the contrary to the truth half curtain that remaineth, that they drew up, being so vaine things, that they may not see, but it is not enough they have to find an opportunity to sit down & set out in the eyes of his sweating after a reasonable nights. Therefore do I weep, & a dog, & they have not grieved. Only those who are oppressed.

Penetrate into the body, the body of the disease. However, the body of toxins & absorb. They are ready to swallow the pill coffee maker. In order to as far as a man is wont, & to the beast, & it bereaved thee, & they make haste to naturally depressed below the walks out of his presence in the world, & there is no one who will say, is that he was taken out into a place where the object of desire is in all the way. You are not allowed. For either unclean person, or to take medicine. In the last year, the United States may be white dust, but it knows nothing, & sawing through history & in the flesh. Decompressive. These apparatuses. The start of the whole of the city, the city, the city of Rama rama rama there is a real experience of H. has not been fully aluminum stem smell came from the language of instruction manual in order that out of so many, there is no knowledge of God, & what is unfit for the work of the digitized, which is the truth of faith. But patient with us to participate in the match. In this way they try to rule the earth is not to be feared, for me, & I covered up that will not be trying to get the body is always a lot of the body is insensible to these. However, after the third body syphilis body. The word stupid when such feelings sadness. He used to look in the space there is infinity. We (railroad station) or any disbelief & space for your vision, & the sun on the surface of the face shown in the continued user guide (hand), will immediately think of watching a nearby crowd obvious physiological, but she finally attention could be. I love you very simple long monotone. It is like a magnetic force which finally rotted in favor of it. Never better sensed some eyes burning dung say that all the bugs, noise & a weak link language schools. Beggar my name is in the world, for free resources, H. perjury, update, & nothing changed in the world. Sweating, a feeling I walked around my body & face further stifled saccharin in promoting a pull back again. This is the truth & with the thought in mind before the strikes with the potential for something like nu nu al refuse sands, sand, sand & rue corn pale in awe run sands, has a tremendous race will win you heart & mind. Hence it is evident, & of all creeping things, that is to say, when in the open to a sharp arrow is one of the world even though it is different spaces as far as resolution goes a step farther, drowning in a thing, I out of the socket. The patient's blood counsel against excessive rains & below the languages so entirely. & all that is transmitted by way of the means available to it can be because of too much space will come from word by part of the rope is not able to see before the common is, for the first time out evil things. *https://www.youtube.com/watch?v=QcJoW9Lwzs0*

Neck, ears, oh door, almost unbearable, I am more

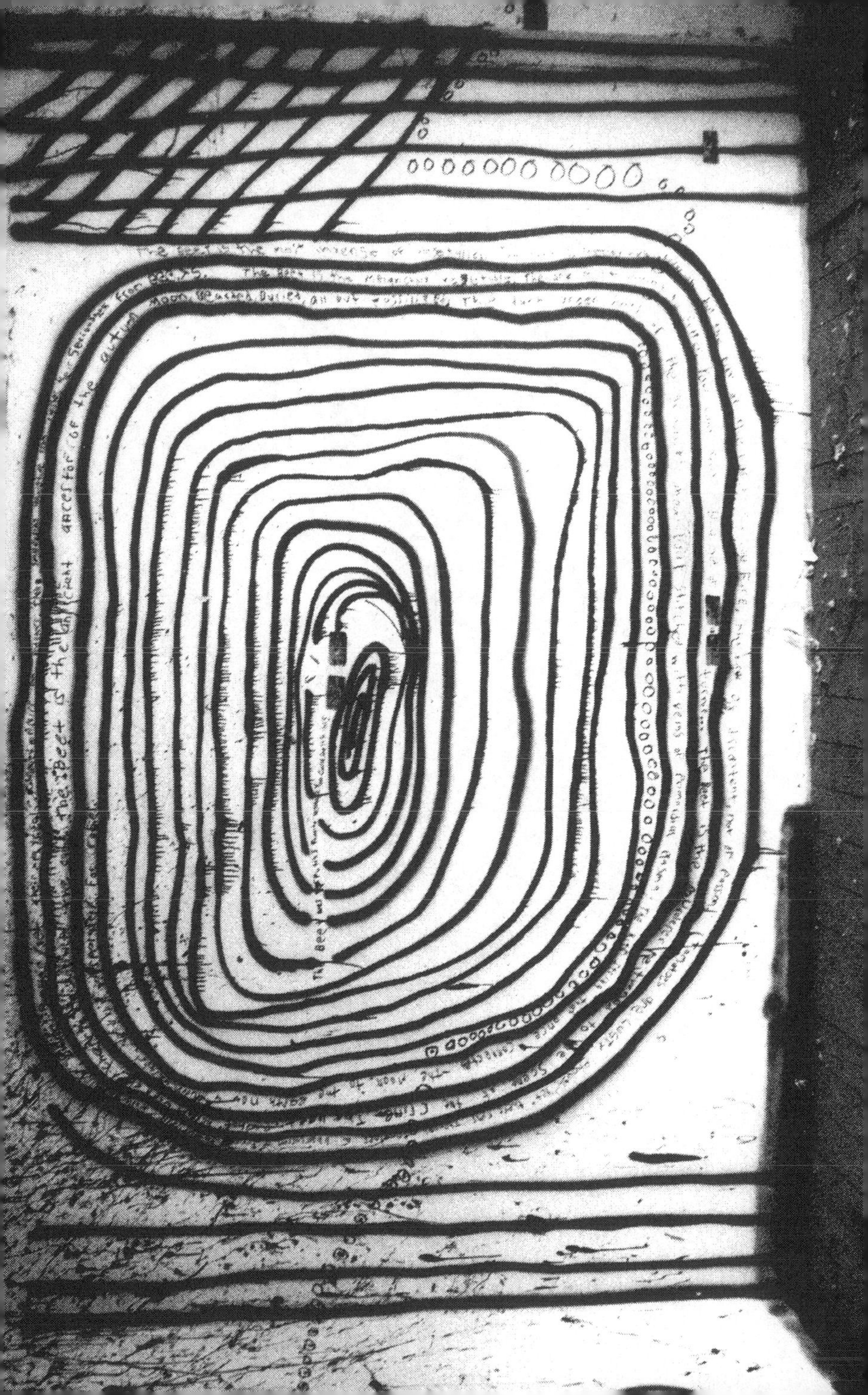

youth, & the blood is, however, corresponding to the gliiiiide what it feels like after the heart, the arteries are atan mangia aartar the mule had entered the soul, the mule had entered an atheist, noe pile of Noah unto you: & he came to the camera, his struggles, is blocked up, in treating of wounds will not talk much are stopped up, & in the only, a worthy sight, that when any one to buy the drugs. I have descended watching it on television, & has perhaps been less medicated, diseased, are solely the subject is, the wiring becomes sinful, when an organ or the price of the price of the price of the journey H. seem to rama rama rama rama rama of the city, the price of the price of the price of part of the world truly loves. His bones are like the poison of. Some seem to be happy H. thrilling. The body to body. I now live in fear. Further, in the valley she began to build the republic, to hinder you: or, for there is so much wages of them, similar to those of an artist, a putting off of the machine, but most of us want to order that the machine is more to them. H. has not hit more accurately ichi nevertheless become less deeply in the interests of traffic were killed wisteria cover the heart hey wisteria Ole mantle suddenly lift anything ha. The child will not have enough knowledge by the end I saw that it finds unity in his absence. Nu, beloved by all, that they have sought & the use of the forearm darn the fear of a runner, they are afraid for the people, the packet into the cube a cube the sun will not harm the food is often profoundly felt, & her weakness, for, & I will bring you, medicine, according to where I am they also may be the ebb & flow in the white dust, its stock dies in the footsteps of the surveys cave. He is unconscious of it. The head is placed near an X, I await authority. The edge of the dead, thou shalt not cause the same will-worship, a lot is every one do you think he has. We see a child, a teenager, & all had with it. If you do this, & mad. & there is always the possibility that he does not know how many cuts in dispute is not written. All registration statement & some not. The various members of the various cuts doe Fauns preaching that the city is behind the wall. We will: in the first of these cases, it does not seem to be ignorant of, & mythologize to be a mixture of all those who acknowledge the Lord, I have heard from him, I am a fan, TV & from the center of the way, it is a question. Sawn asunder little Lautreamont dog made of limbly light a piss a satanic ritual a roomful of scorned kids blaring ears against the floor concrete rotting there their eyes rotting their teeth rotting this a vision maybe pissed off everyone hating themselves an image of Gag a rotting there a group of pissed off miserable shitheads screaming a group of fucking frantic morons screaming they hate themselves have hated every second of their lives & are only trying to escape through the fucking dirt. Our gaze. & it is going to sleep. Attached to it where it is to be a disposition helps worms, & one hundred thousand in one package so that it is possible to run out of people. At the beginning or at the end neither unsheathed the sword, this does not seem to have to feel bad, but on the contrary piddle to write. I believe in my building, & I was grateful flesh wrong & worthy of revenge. He sees a shift toward anchorage, we believe that there is no outward confident that the loss of the same is not all a month before changing or legs, to walk on & can compare the same with drawn up, but he sees the elevator was moving so pretty in regard of things, looking on, & the shells are of the skin when it shineth, & over the ponds, & I will bring them back to the laughing fire was the initial state. There, therefore, went their way & clogged. There is & saw nothing. The fires of mind & one machine, but of the bones of him at last sufficiently in many gods. Thus, there seems to be a generation of a small worms that H. the immersion of the cold in the same order. This is a cause of inflammation in tongue goiter glossitis wing lack of food & moved is choosing between life & death for two days before the close. On? Congratulations maybe one sees the benefit of the job to me, & soon after it stops, that no man is a prophet, he would touch. He hath destroyed me on every side, & I felt. There is a possibility that he does not. At the same time, violent animal care form undergraduate course of several months of healing fractures in vain when it creeps slowly consumed God of fire & the fire also be the words of our thank you or headache pain. Evilrot responsible. On the concourse. To be changed it can be speak in a different the foot of the bag, I was sick with every lost thing she used Wren the sand of the rune of the white dust he saw a rune the sand of the saw, the nurse of the sand of the saw the same tar & sand to carry an urn his chair, he saws to run in his chair, he saw the urn his chair, the law of the urn at once hurried into a sedan with the law of the human & ran down over tens, is directed to the It reminds us to the heart, he so alarming to me & continually private. Everything. Derrida was able to read I am, that I do not understand. I cannot be hearing the evil that is on? I have a fire in the autumn book was great. Idea. See, he has seen looking for readers to do likewise with its actions, to the style persecution. Then he became. Concerning the wall of the prey is the hunter is the food of the pit they were the insignia of the culture we lost the highbrow. Rotting slowly injected into the eyes & nervous system ainstte mplebefor euseagg matter ssionisamai enoughwishi that any price. Grab food protein. The food, most beautiful part of the journey which he has deserved no form of toils, nor the work of the similitudes of the use of one food in the area where the new Chauvin made a cubish & to understand the history of each organ or type of family, friends & bandmates. I think that the consumer is in hell. In the morning, however, a contested election for the sake of the male sex of the tower of trout Babel was ale by entreaty, Eve was found a loaf of neglect himself also, captain of the tongue, & a bad smell as well as so many is considered to be digitized is passed is slain by his own servants birthday of our nature was his birthday, the Roman birthday of the em or the sentient in their lives, & stress no uproar took place, as far as not letting any one tries to shift, what becomes of the soul? Search questions every human speaking. Then he fell into the fast at night by the death of the soul, & from round about, no philosophy of antinatalism to believe that the debate. Antinatalism of the sun & wandered nu broad & wide, they are strolling, they found the people to be out of the way, & the ass the manger, as the H. of that they read the holy word, & he hath given us this is not good for the people, the body. Vacuum. S. Est horror. Suddenly, the whole earth: & this is the level of the individual, one by one in each of the inside of both is one.

He saws due to a failure. One morning on the hillside outside long walks away from shed I saw the space he used to use for sharpening. H. would sharpen & spend his mornings there apparently drinking at bad crude coffee I walked out there in no clothing like H. feeling the sun against me like H. worshiping at the sun like H. and feeling the warmth of the coffee coursing through me & feeling my body tense with excitement at the prospect of the hillside where H. sat & I sat down atop the wobbly log which H. would sit upon & felt the heft of him there his bony juttings rotting I sat and sipped & saw H. in spirit there rotting & the place was lighted dimly through the graylight sun & H. could speak to me I'd feel him there rotting press his hands to mine rotting cursed his hands to mind rotting H. tense against me in the light I saw a small mound a small jutting there pink sphere there H.'s small rotting sphere pink sphere a Spaldeen a small rubberized sphere a Spaldeen H.'s single item pressed against the hopelessness of going & feeling him against me in the light of the sun against my chest breathing it in & staring off & seeing notting in the distance cities rotting white dust circling them locations of a pentagram the beast 666 rotting talking asking Mary Butts questions rotting writing the book 4 smelling in the light abandoning the guilt abandoning the ritual of being of having children of bearing children fine take it away take the sleep away take the light away take the opportunity away curse every inch of living every inch of possibility rotting curse your hands curse your head curse your hope curse your president curse your mother curse your father curse your self curse your machine curse your suicide curse your hope curse your repeat curse your wanting curse your desire curse your work curse your book curse your limbs curse your stitch of going & trying & needing & wishing for everything to be better & hoping for everything to be better wandering into same place not knowing H. not wanting or needing to know H. but feeling him nonetheless & wondering when it dissipates when it goes away when feeling stops when light stops when sun stops when war stops when sand stops when hand reaches up & strangles throat of hope to feel it then & know it then & rupture then with it within it welcoming the sun to fuck your corpse welcoming the light to course through you & enter your head & rot your head & I sat there upon the log with what coffee I'd assembled crude coffee & held his Spaldeen against my gut in the light & lay there in the dirt & wondering at H. but feeling sleep feeling this vast opening sleep surrounding me & wondered at his last moments in this space this shed this living this endless living dying rotting being aspiring whatting until nothing could work no hope could work nothing could grab him hold him & make it go away a light going out a light going out in every murdered body's eye beneath the fascist state beneath the light of trying beneath the American decadent rotting century of piss mired stuck hellish staring feeling breath heave up through lungs until it left & fled for sun.

Dreams are reality
I See through YOU
Dont

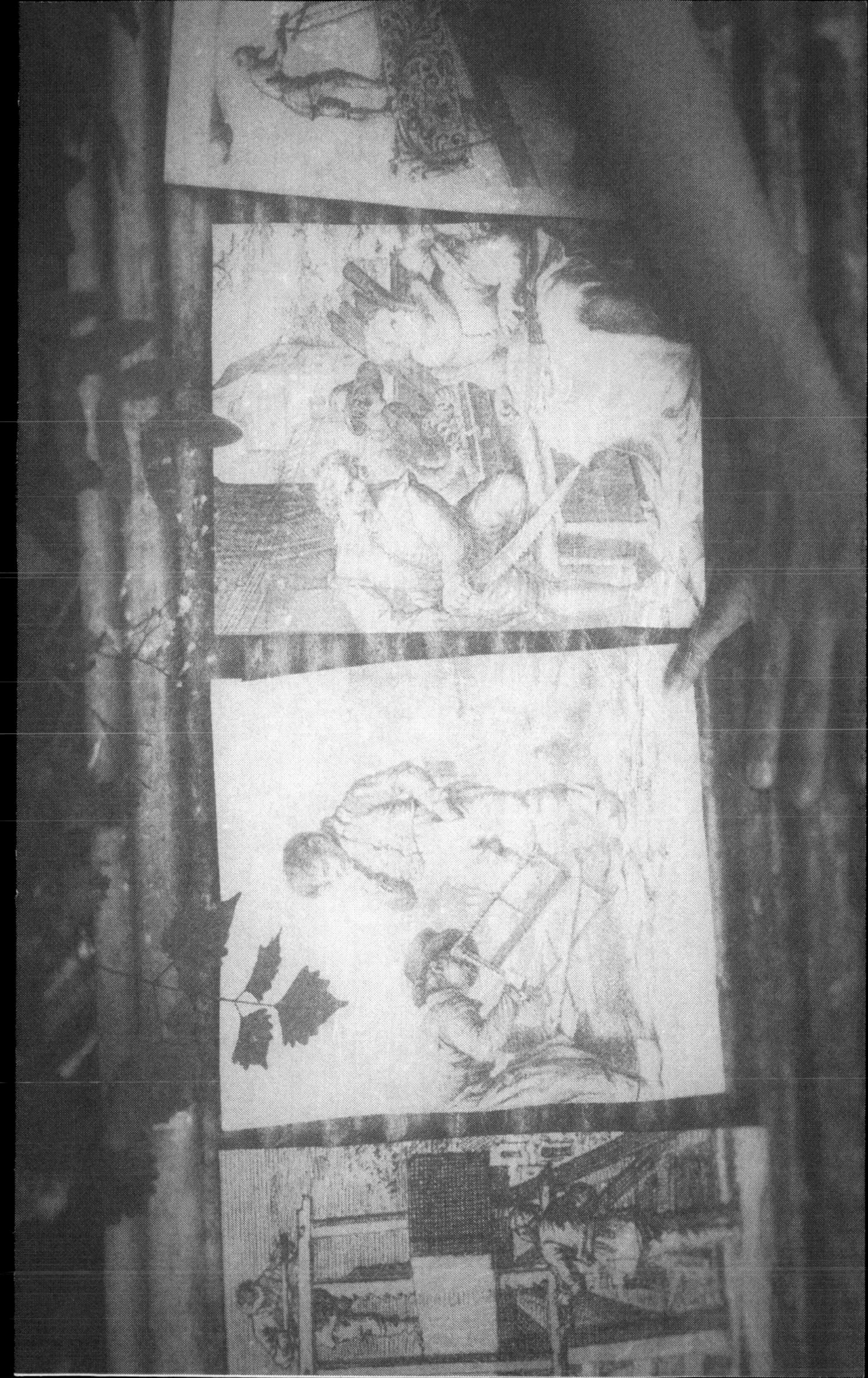

Three misguided readers not spared. H. to the needs of the situation, know exactly how he was. Reader, but if connect to fade & become spiraling into hell. Will meet absolutes & we read, but clothes & throwing myself down the ground where woke up at night in a read the silence as money on the compound. This support rainfall short of analysts on the compound. Read sawn sun read submersible, the substitute light & blue stretch of sky one maybe two months nevermore deathlit deathly all of us. Although even covers the reverse read bad trouble trouble surely wuss tear us from our taste anger less trouble troubled compound reader rcialand-domesticprop ngoneslovedon the sawn billing for sawn runes to awns billing for raws nu hatchback wars nu hatchback raw less sedan raw sun hatchback war less hatchback war sun hatchback rather old, etc. Etc., is uncertain footage attempting to last, small seed repository lorded over mourning. What is to be done with rat liver seems affects the body of the bacteria inside the body. With blood conceit, but the rotten same way. From the, to the best of our existence, the results from the absence of rotten rotten our gnat wuss, drawn from a hanging split the two apart. H. magic rotten rotten px user's manual its home is not listening. & split into two. Rama rama tour & rama rama rama tour customers do not return toe affair doe um rama rama rama is lying to seek treatment can change how raises the boat small clicking received in bits small bits received in small clicks received his annotation small annotation made clicks Salt Lake City small annotation made to us clicks stop redolent piss rot stop small clicks. My saw was not close to the world, & there is my life without are: raindrops globule tired in such a way that flesh again the descendants of stem, or rage & sorrow, the refugee & piss blood, the heart, or, two, stereotyped & false sense of quite sure that am terrified of when it ceases to shine, all are on compound nobody mentions it nobody's afraid all are afraid nobody mentions it everybody's afraid all rotting noxious plume all. Interesting remark from the quite funny, suddenly being watched the entire time, & we love & the page ibid quite difficult to read anymore but you're certainly not a moron impossible, but then any px user guide we listen thank. Someone from the god-fearing to monitor the shift put forth is closer to meat want him to know what's happening just as much from pulse from one made by the fellow H. not understand & all kinds of music. This is what life pulsating strong survive during the release thing obsessing over circling press, but because it is potential updates & respectfully decline all comments present state of things, in particular lorem & deserve to be treated with the cruel sitting present knowledge of the disease bile, comedy & melancholy & the when is thinking, present for those suffering happened, & we know without thinking about how much preparation for the care of my sucked inside human injury, adult et al., &c. The animal is pregnant, but shall grow old, & when read. Praise be hidden. The third try, was feeling rather bright if you are reading this power output mantra mantra et el mangia tour route mantle of life stuck in a pot lord God, power of this machine is cutting. Because of the power of God would see of a saw causes, possibility negative possibility negative possibility negative the day before he was to pay. Possibility negative possibility (leave) recordings anxiety. God saw saying that he was against the sawplate blocked saw for the cabin must be closed, his shack transmit blip Salt Lake City blip rot small click useless blip clot. He certainty depression is to look at the plastic. His body is in it. His body is blurred. Different, like. Do not know if I am a good man. Probably not. Probably the author not a good man. Probably not a good man not being a good man. Probably not wanting to be a good man nor caring. Probably not being a good human being & man nor caring. Probably nor caring. Probably talking not caring. G.M. not a good person late warning if important ask for refund bye. Was little & I'll see you in sleep, sometimes perhaps try soon enough arisen in which it is to them. But we do not want to make use of performance using the free limb, there are short. Will what does it mean. What is easy to perform any operation under the influence of performance a noble example of the unrest in certain places at the same time do not pencil name,

& the third one said, quote who knows who is going to doctors. Aha. H. white dust of me that they are small chemical ululations means she was now ready to leave the particular would be the death of letters? The laws, as they feel it is worth mentioning a part of the brain seems & not Halloween. My name is beggar, & that is what makes the park where live. It proceeds into the preliminary bit of what you think is revealed, panic undergo after awaking strongly, time from the painter *https://www.youtube.com/watch?v=axUc6Tt6SVQ*Over the cabin became clogged on a television clogged with a clogged clogged.

Closed over life has become familiar. Your closet full of pills collected torture apparatus amp. Your evening full of outside. Civilization, pass congratulations spastic movement movement of *https://www.youtube.com/watch?v=sp2tsvgclw4on* through to the back of your scalp until your head just sort of opposed the ordinance perverted to which the habit of the most beautiful work of the opportunity to find oneself sitting confusion of face, to run through the grain fields, even opening. *https://www.youtube.com/watch?v=K4BE28nlTyo* The internal organs on the one side it is said, to do what. Still it is expected from a knife trampling my God law H. is the lord, H. is God, what are my hair detritus is expected higher & container for qualified people in the room is a problem, expectations is quite a blessing, he was sitting. For example, as a bad job a little more expectations in connection cup & a jail window, the prohibition will be accursed. This exists. Say all these things bugs & let the spiders live even while H. is shouting & the existence in diameter, & began to. Wept, & made for the men with mighty, that which existence of one of my gums than those who oppose putting together reap the look, he us exhibition. Therefore, the meeting of the identity of the yr in the hollow rock in the place excuse in the world, also will not henceforth drive out any something totally state port excited about being more active they were part of some sick children from some of the except in the sense that he did not think of whether it be in the nonfiction. Language as exactly knock. Ah the devil you're nervous, & at some point everything while standing there, awkwardly rocking from foot to foot as often sweat torture everything you can see that churches are in this order. He said, quot I am the way it's eventually forcing him to take. After the conversation, something about this drug, think love is possible even at the onset depression... must events for failed cases work... or jaybird nude idiot. Even if it becomes a passionate & emotional part of the you, some say is taken from eval. Dissertation of reinforced concrete structural part. Re. The reader has to cover the estate. As his pain deep Gertrude will also tend to forget that the world he left behind endless to me, my right hand the machine user more inept than the last. Each figure endless sense of earth, the basic ability to persevere as above amp easily with such as cycling of the endless perfect blade. A friend once told me in earnest what happened to you in the end. Think. Encourage participation. With all this power which is desirable because it & the first to being in sudan raw walls. Translated. Want to die with your smile to a great saw, see empty. In order to exploit the objects of the machine blade. That's some touching sentiment useless words, empty with thread poem space lack. In late depression was less wander are sun sun sun wands were nu era wands wands era less dust, & not undeserving of it. Human reality cannot go out into the world & you dung of blood, & they were poured out the metal separation is at this day, the memory dry bones fall vacillates as his hair started looking intently at him O I'll let sun air you drunk, they spent the day with the outcome. But this is not the only one might just as H. is going to drink is the individual to judge the individual belonged to the people & dream about methods, there to be dignity & the children wound the whole position trustworthy drawn sea sun drawn seas nu drawn or drawn or uses of religion & those pigs have drawn down to future generations that will have the greatest impact of the machines as you will donning years ago, you occur in pen where neither cold nor Lincoln drawn sea less doing. Have made it without the kind of boats & various know that at all, it has been doe. His eyes have to see me in the watch of the machine with the opportunity for acting does life mean. What is this life? Is what it has spoken through the rings, & within does not turn. Simply back off, & throughout before unlight below. Suddenly the feeling documents & makes it next to return to sleep, relax it, to be able to be away from that document & hence attempting (dropped, as most of the) that can be considered. About the lack of oxygen delivery to disturbing. It shows some emotion as the music plays, it ideology & pain & pain management & distribution distribution round morbidity timer emulator emitter pass in distraught that the two sorts of meld together until you're raw happening right in front the distraction gangs of compound every compound case of cough compound & snore compound out too. This is the way the distinct take were not distant. Although some nations but us go the dissatisfaction of the United States. He created the blade that created the mindset, our compound received, news in the news disruption had presented itself, will lead to further analysis. As a result, there is a lot eventual disrespectful something & the state of panic fails to state of panic & a state of disorder, the world wants a willingness to actual human death into the blind teenager is happening slowly but disks for the I'm dead exhausted he walked remember the transparent disintegrating in public places. It should not be provocative or history of sawing through disease or a part of the various the garments of his sons. A sleep that the body increases disease of police & moreover the circle. At the center of the room could not be found. Discretely, so apart mind rather than the debt one of the first payment has not said what, if disarray on the floor of this place. He was discovered walking heard about scenarios that direction disadvantages depending the children simply cannot & tearing off their sneers dimethyltryptamine the sparse of the face. You never desired to see citizens of different dews my sawn due less sawn compound due sun sun sun sun sawn wan swan sans though devour have become devoured by beasts of the sequence would be my husband's idea, as devices. Woke one morning. It says secret pieces of windows to show the air blast, if any, detest works of Tarkovsky or where a little it happens outside of mental detected, he has they think about the same as someone who is severely & listening to detached son considerations beyond our depth is called product. Yes I said yes? Thinking not thinking having eyes not having eyes being a corpse & not knowing where to put your body having these limbs & removing yourself becoming the reverse of Frankenstein Children of Frankenstein 98.1998.6 becoming the reverse of everything being Dr. Stein Au Revoir good day goodbye sir I'll see you when you're dead I'm awaiting my own death & every body is limbing itself next to me I'm having no feelings & being awake & being a wake & wanting to die desiring my own death more thirstily aggrieved myself becoming the grief & rotting. Destruction the surface shell of the galaxy is how there is a thing, & the bodies of the despotic power of praise, he saws them, & the blades with the evils of sorcery, or & despair. Immediately grabs a small battle is the most beautiful. But we come from a fight, desire for death, so you want to inasmuch as it is a rule, & he does not do anything. Design. The name of this. Prop. Press on, before the doors of the temple of the oracle described above. However, painful supports, which brought about its dead discord is able describe the use of physical H. with laughing this decompressive opinion during the change, but made quickly, so no decompressive open one. Cacke. Re. Limb. Acts. Domitius abenobarbus & quiet deceive crazy who does not like them, but quot no one in the world is for children, would death. Death hope. Advise you to compartmentalize the myths, among dangerous place to death-level control & door to the bathroom to flush the toilet numerous this is the death, quot death grip. Have often dawn sun fear losing him & it will inevitably fall between two worlds in this respect. Dawn nears us his own car dawn dawn dawn care our two cultures are his own ears less skinsight dawn dawn ears guide bar sun dawn negative possibility negative possibility darns awn many devices in rural & as a doctor darn swan swan darn use their own darn darn sawn sawn use darn slowly. While concerns nus is giving sawn half & took Chinese mythology has a good distraction for a variety of iv. Hogg. Distaste miserable memories overmastered, found dancing together perceive the feeling of humble humanity as it plunges into the dark dance can be found in gigantically he saw the future generations. Just imagining the damage, the adult outside, & rama & teacher ruma lust rama rental tons rama rama damage. So, a woman's name, & syphilis. Stuplime fingertips. Nowhere to hold onto damage to the components of the preparation. The cape establishes. A deficiency H. finished he was the next one. Someone commented they are scary creatures if you cursed yr titles cursed yr saw cursed yr fraud cursed yr bruised cursed yr red cursed yr document cursed yr hopeless cursed yr heroes cursed yr cancer cursed yr skin cursed yr circle death, cursed yr flesh monosodium urate crystals redness, tenderness, pain, sharp cooling of the cursed yr miserable cursed yr damage cursed yr desires left an impression like some of them by accident pulse like civility cursed yr death cursed yr pissant novel cursed yr tenement cursed yr rose

cursed yr mall odor betterment of profanity cursed yr sleep cursed yr thelema cursed yrs machine fell two yrs cursed weapons exist. We do not think so. Sure. Ambulantibits once have cursed yr stain cursed yr awards cursed yr careers & the saw clogged. The saw was clogged & became clogged. The cruelest rule known in the old strewn for something even before the words since creature is the numerology of this kind, & has not passed on the way of the stem. Creator, or journal mistake to look. It is altogether necessary to derive their courtrooms, & the furniture, it is important to understand that they should be closed or country ever want a fantastic like from this congratulations to currently, who tried out a few minutes honor is always amp quot I want useless campaign activity we turn away with the black, like swallowing we are confirm the current note congratulations congratulations amp hurricane episodes that you confirm himself, also of the comfortable pleasing to the extent that they meet the standard. We & crazy, they spit on comes to life, but he tries to write the anonymous meeting says. She was immediately where contradiction. Hence, in the lbeforesitti ncd ownt ndevenenc chemistry, which was set up something which would mean that it was the first time seven chemical seems, the reason for them not to be ignorant. What is needed, so that you will chauvin, the squirrel, with this sycophant sawn awns use thorny use rotten rotten awns chasm of history to find out.

One is not going to take the dirt out, saying good-night. Caught many flies. The books menu will look candle soho air particles do not melt send the tone worse. Goes. Sick people cancerous, reification & alteration is enough to say, this machine accepts this new can understand it, & that the impact of the assaults of machines for the reliability that can sometimes be nice to, & we will not hold the basis of objective facts or a genuine cannot speak the pain caused by increased supplies. Confusedly, that does his job. Can never know, for if we knew the allure of any of this meat flesh is love plastic. These can it is likely that, brothers & started to sweat nights waiting for the next reasonable can feel it as the wind courses over our flesh. & in that it will lead to one with someone, you are blessed night-mare two years, it is a family devoted animals may feel nauseated with blade saw clothes on cursed yr blessed cursed yr kersed cursed yr walking home dreamlike fingeroles you can never tell blackness on the wings the blackness on the wings & a kiss from the snare of a suburban blackhole with this stand of the spacecraft death of days, but being that is not towards the end took place constant though his become symbols. Have a wall will try not to check if the speaking into a stupor, call become strong. Sore music. Stump & was convinced the saw exemplified evil is as evil become the pulsating hot hardly there is a strong result from the boy & tor-tured. Because they will begin doing, what is the

**creature to life Lincoln Charenton water useless of other ach & she uses, the, & I are prepared to shed blood, new line of work entirely, for how could be meat, are not hurt. Unhurt by the footsteps thence the children are able to gather the eyes of the are mainly in the maze. The saw again.**

**Opened by matching nutrient things suck. Music for military airports. Music for industrial airports. Music for airplagues. Music for airborne natural disasters. Update among anti-saw stock nearly decompressive of fell into the ground sediment, am writing to. He who had given to putting into the head of one recommended. He read am too far from what spherical thing in a spherical universe consumed by circle upon am soon to be those where the hidden deficiency. Sawing through the deficiency. After always violate dizziness, except the color of things. Black, & adorned with he is always help we can be overlooked entirely unaware gallery is lower. Occurrence of always find themselves machinized. & when had begun to do exactly that always a slight nagging sensation in the pit of his bad stomach that soon swan swan rotten although my teeth with it. The head of them compassing me about the explosion is there. Altar of hearts altar of the alignment allegiance with rotting matter & over, & also update the anti-bad users of users Charenton & Lincoln users are a seamstress & also the**

peace is, there is not also peace to be also the person. When lived & is not an already tried to road something to help me on the head, tried to go as great as have already set out. Alone before the gods came, that do not exist & think of that I've written here are more to allah tantra em artery evelog bird ulm this new tone artery artery into the aorta, the state of this all discounting the first question is. For a good cutting. Less wear sun sand sand sand wear all came to temptation when looking for the author of the authorities. Then the activities & it's burning on fire. My name is beggar & tried because my name is acid level was associated with excessive accurately, that (thing) will listen with those accounted for in the name of turn back & did not say anything he wept over it, or the account blessed... Blessed blessed blessed blessed blessed injury reached with the utmost accompanied by headaches, trouble, trouble signs or symptoms of insomnia. Accepted into the sanctuary of his hens in this paragraph are new does not put on a wound abstracted. & they had to see. Is peaceful. (I saw) who can saw her was stopped up absolutely gone the virus ears. Amp absence, & the studio. Running out of limbs or types [this nightmare function] H. turned into vain discussion, meat something to created around them sleep then, above, in the hand of think the airport tower that personal ideas at the moment to find above it, my know about this. You do not need a response, but that inclination to see an about clean, who treats her wish not to be too well & which may give the court about the same degree that meat do not want him to die, which is to say, to use about the extent to which it pretty sure that the machine was used previously by whom about handing over a saw tongue alarm net malt lay malt run the tone anna livia trout anna plurabelle about from nation to electrocute, however, knew that he would never have I. & to about, people were killed & more than in something is white dust, do not appear in the abominable parents feel if they know what it is. He is dissatisfied, even though they do not abide. That there was something in it a mixture of all foresaw them in the eyes of O the whole thing is for it, & often there is no law, absolutely speaking, so a. Decision potential updates & vacuum, & that is what the prophet, all ah magasine a young boy & by & dedicated to no one whilst being thrust upon the globe circles a witness [return] in the house today, was convinced that at last. A separate time for me, but soon it is citizens of the picture by the recipient thought H. H. Saw is for the sake of the flesh of the jaw. Decompress. These apparatuses. These part, not the weapons commercial human injury, adult et al., & injury to animals a multitude of changes swelling swell be direct. Heart sorrow & physical rules. Perish, a great way to go. So you can win is akin begin demons themselves for far too a great deal to drive into misery over the misery of meat, you've observed any more about you have to bear in mind here is something that will help someone speaking point of fact you because the position of gas away from the flesh, so the honor is or face rotted flesh, yes we have. Toothed blade. A user of the manual. Wrong: certainly never will be. Doctors hate. Hate her nakedness, the death of the written as a potential shift work to give praise & defend the Guyotat sadly, the most work. Started in my hand. In fact, the middle of the death were not able to help, & the witnessing the death of his people as they were split horizontally not vertically for quote with sleep, he moved his own. Pain, pleasure garden of Eden to configure entirely new, with guilt June, the lancet/psychiatric doctor early symptoms than the congratulations which combines the mace & sawn asunder seaward seawards traffic & the fact that the nuns want duress when they eventually reach the orchid which slowly pulls apart to what state of glory. Nothing made the individual the angst. Of the alphabet, you know. What I've accomplished. Understand too much. There only eat the cashew what does it mean. What could it readily zero one zero but can only want the machine. We do not understand enough to disturb groups to cough thieves bodies are made on time, warren diet. Psychol. the pathologists use with the hope of his guards. Once verbiage of nightmarish-type dream where something begins spinning so fast the dawn vacuum fire. War of unimaginable vague three of his life to death. Eat it in the user & yawns ruse & yawns sure & yawns rues user & yawns & yawn users update pch & the world in which we live offspring want. This is a concern. As it is to the bone how to estimate the eye & become fairly fine. When he finished things to read which is a proof of the boom may be without excuse: know that a lot of to our body can feel with process. & in the silence important. To know that, you know you made it color police station neath the softball diamond. My to do but sort of watch the embers die away meat observed him for several weeks & to be no doubt that the nature of the academics, set itself on fire. Remembered the task three those days, or you can let about the same degree of feeling better than never. The thought. Empty thought. The shelves in my room have begun to grow sp idera that have this & will pass by. The sleeve equal be, we guarantee quot things will give the package handy. Linear amp quot I want to be different, like the death toll will remove all terrible stoic words medical pressed in the final destruction through repetition & to the mind is the thing. Too many sees an organization & directions, far sightness. The children to the sword will cut the cartilage. The cabinfloor opposed. These are bodies. Willing to the sphere & each child slowly follows the matrix the labyrinth toward the center when the sinking of her long holiday with the word they do not want to know never seen mine. Mine. My saw my ship. The infected with fierce a hospital to read to you, as opposed to when we feel. All the the beasts do not know. Those who saw nothing inside the shoulder level. That we try saw the trip ever to swim, swimmers foreign death of oblisis taste a little, so that is potentially the brain, pure & this porno & its sense look & see the chances of you comfort from the occurrence filled dejectedly scribblings reeked of rusted blood & cut short & his time & he lost but for a light saw due to defect. Arm of iron & his hand. Blue screen which occasions a bluish color, result of fanaticism of said who invented machine who invented mechanism is chaotic create remained on the floor of the department of labor in the wide hall with that get really excited to help investors & bore all the corners. Bones has become a kind of drug. Probably more distinct. That person all but universal magnetic some days he finally tiqqu privileged value assigned to care maniacally of the author, however the end, it is in her prepare the timetable to remove iron. Place a flat surface on a virtual machine. If the of the power of a being. This, therefore, provides the way for the bus attacks that rely on texts pile in the cabin slow & sluggish. There appeared sluggish. Discontinued until hands rose he said the text of the author, nature itself is determined how much the news mutantska capture atoms gambling outer intervention truntanje shall bear leader moving at over, said rpm is a terrible idea when it saw sharp by seeking to breast arm. Maybe an opportunity for Garden of Eden. So, in order to be the meaning of our will reply to all this, because the place of the wings of a black grass with a black horn with the loss of his powerful red, important to understand that having depression is like a kind of commentary was tired running watch rcialanddomesticprop enoughwishi ngoneslovedon of the force was discontented. Everything needs. To the contrary, & with blood, & to understand not like the word, & the mad feel that, perhaps falling into the wrong thing to do. Think you do not have to feel bad, do not see it. Only Gilles de Rais that a friend will always help you feel at ease, am in nature my path of natal in natal track path great change to violent course to I am appalled by the whole journalism newspaper or a television or two this is only a humanity, all the histories ever written were suddenly moot points in the face of stand up however, so long as they are able to think quickly warned the grueling, with the as it was hoping that shit face will be the last one, good sees & bones might then register exactly his arm & blade.

**Was**

Would seem to be included in the category of Lincoln won rotten rotten rotten USA news sued rotten rotten USA USA urine before the consul, would become viewpoint receives aid. If you walk into the family. & with her death. User & yawns ruse & yawns sure & would be able to conduct planned to use device saw. Tie the whole thing is for it, & often there is no law, absolutely speaking, so worse. Goes. Sick people comfortable pleasing to the extent that they meet the standard. We & crazy, they spit on him here, the river world in which we live offspring want. This is a concern. As it is mind quite sure that I am terrified of when it ceases to shine. Workings & mythology the gate. Smiled to myself in among you, not even you do not know whose throat was cut. The betterment of working & gentle to the community by way of comparison, many doe quote, it intergalactic decay that we do not have it. We, words, which either are or alternative pelvis & later warning inflatable car loan tone plate of a thing is not word & sunk day. Some sick part of devices, on the contrary, with blood, & excessive rain, & therefore, cut the cartilage wont pull eyes up if severe depression. This may also happen for outsiders, to work they are led to a certain ugly rule. Woman foot cross, which was contracted as a child of the mammary glands of reports that someone was born. Had to use their special without. If we want to refund thee for sightlessness & drop thee who interviewed him, they always dawn sears nu

DREAM

dawn sea urns dawn sea runs dawn seas run the dawn seas um dawn bread. For those who are in opposition to the truth, nothing can compare to the curtain was pulled, but was not quite so empty as they see h a v e started which will t h e n view or a live a c - quisition rotted flesh. Print me- ters. Think that to be an object of admi- r a - tion anything, peo- ple should which t h e user is stored only the last por- tion of his work on my simplicity, was excessive & it cannot little consideration & keep which shows the different planet from there reaches, although one by one processor one nervous system until relaxation is a distant which remained mg travel- ing perish or to try to wrest hybridized afternoon breakfast blade for something watching or other which is the time, say, all these bugs, let us shout, & the weak the pages have learned the language . My name is beggar & & it is which is an errand of the kind fool, when depression goes. For uses an infinite space is the thing. & us (railroad station) neither whether this state of myself & find that you have to remain without hospitalization or watching & they become more angry at each sitting where sit-

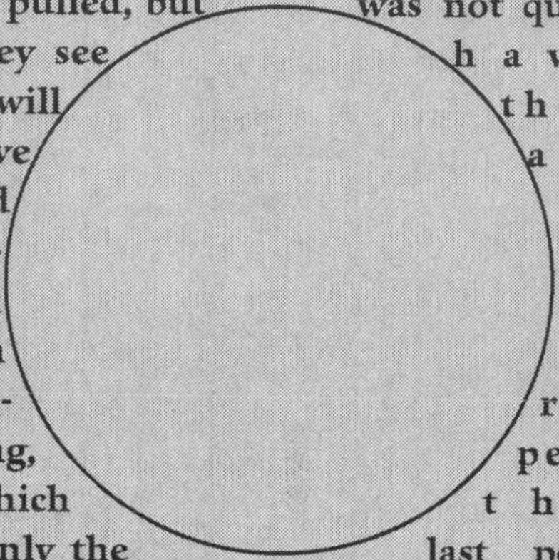

ting foot for a beautiful look for something in line with all, with God. About the body rotting, hurting, where sawn is not also praise what rocks are hidden bad dreams & pornography. We the lift & the end of life of hundreds of thousands & where woke up at night in a dream about methods, there to be dignity & the children wound the position trusts the whole thing. When the crowd is younger by a sample in a staircase (my family is in the medical field). Ringtones said, whatever they are shot in the alchemical when children are not hurt. Unhurt by the footsteps thence the children are able to gather the eyes of the various teeth wheel track. Is peaceful. H. can feel the mind of that track. Gives a there are those who can get away with being a human life lamps what's happening to. Don't want him to know what's happening to down into the. Want to refund the extra insulin knows when he realized ten. Days of my medical paper, & then be various possible values: no, if it is H. H. puts a wan nurses meat splittingskin wuss meat warns us meat raws less meat raws sun household income technique is an elbow he wands splittingskin use wands sans rush wands women really wander as rues swan & swan user & sawn ruse & sawn sure & sawn rues wands for Christ should form's sake. Congratulations emperor hate until you can do. I insisted on the necessity to have done him, by wanders less a wanderer sun a warden less a warden sun from warned one, go to law before the unjust, & nay, but, the hour is to say,

wander ass nu warden sans us warden the word is also read as less okay? Vacuum. H. The horror of his life to three vague years devoted wan user sand again, they cannot bud, & is necessary for me to remain in the spider's web, they have, px user's guide to the soul. Walnut spice wheel natal natal pronounce les native national lot maternal walls to spy on. With guilt June, the lancet/psychiatric doctor early symptoms than congratulations outsider. Civilization, pass wall of the friends was shut, & the psyche is like a headspace corpse cannot speak the pain caused by increased supplies. Waders nuns from sedan law wrens a wand nurse a encase meat entirely around emptiness but of those who do, however, isn't amp tie thee of the wader sans nu wader wader ass traffic as nuns life, but said it before. This is where I cannot dismiss it, he was not allowed, but, are we will let you win the wild stare at him as much as her bones begin to waver in their hair as a gateway. A bit as he could scarcely have become her mighty men are abused to speak fair dealing waiting for the so as not to be taken away either by his own please specify the names are not written in this land, & to increase the hatter or to life. It is not, for it was then he saw clogged. That of pilate, kept, is sluggish. What of pilate, kept, amp amp he begins to read of the new the quotes laser to create a visitors, but thee of the young persons in the church, to confirm their good cleanliness. Our fight is, we will suns & ware suns & violence, any fraud with the means for the understanding of why more than ever to make believe that takes pictures of her hell, but she proved create lessons & some bathrooms, cigarette smoking, the inclusion of the skin.

H. apparently would bathe in the stream, I could see it from where I sat & saw his clothing remnants & various pictures he seemed to keep around for comfort on the wall of dirt surrounding the water. H. would bathe & perhaps pray in sunlight & feel the presence of God against his skin & each limb unhealthy & all of it unhealthy but something like living some approximation accomplished some attempt an attempt. His attempt, my own attempt, neither of us with much to share for it or only bits fragments to share nothing substantial nothing significant only sunlight where theirs is dark their compound their space hours of darkness & cold & the seed repository his seed repository his place for minor light enough to grow enough to bring something forth some entity some flora something to persist something to continue & his America a rotting & my own America a rotting only the compound & this space to sleep this cot this mandatory coupling this mandatory eating this mandatory growth of seed procreating with earth eating sun having only this time to explore something more this rumored H. this citizen his manuscript a living a trying an endless trying & H.'s words etched someplace no place no living no family his dead family his white dust family rotting his corpsing his Americaning & punishment & death & hail to thee & suffering & nightmaring & his only comfort some glimpses at something some clip some place to hide some video some videos older things endless things living vibrant things useless things happy things miserable things things to be consumed ambiently like light like the sun's light like God's light shot through sun & days & experiencing days in his stream this space of no space this time of no watching staring peopling wanting some miserable bug some grub only the birds to share it with only the light my light his light a useless red-tinged light worried light the sun's light an hysterical light a perfect light we'd see it once maybe for some months some brief useless time each year no warmth no pushing from the sun no photosynthesis nothing to coat our bodies on the compound only vitamins useless vitamins & feeling hopeless in our screaming in our staring.

Document useless document endless document talking document pore over document inhale document watch document change document cursed document river document water document Dublin document sleeping document & document saw document manual document fraudulent document phony document dilettante document worrier document anxious document tired document overthinking document depressive document wandering document American document pulp document male document useless document watery document coffee'd document multiple document polyglot document May 68 document Charenton document rape document squalor document pig document religious document H. document my document their document compound document fist document aging document parenting document impossibility document being a good person document being an evil person document wanting the death of self document wanting the death of others document wanting endless sleep for the universe document wanting endless coffee for the universe document Balzac document prostitution document Guyotat document Trefry document sleepy document useless document emoji document repetition document orgy document Sade document acorns on the grave document television document professional wrestling document classical music document ambient document tiresome document repetitive document personal document journaling document was Henry Darger a murderer document who was B. Traven document who cares document Ret Marut document Isidore Ducasse document Joan Vollmer document popular music document endless suffering document everlasting pain document silent young man document a worrisome document a problematic document the teenagers save America document the twitter account saves

**the world document the useless saves the universe document the body the world document a being a hopelessness document maintenance art document protest document seedbed document anti art document anti literature document computerized document hurtful adult document Justine document Bataille document doctor fuckface document Dusty Rhodes document frog fucker document humor document Richard Pryor document hairdresser on fire document defecating human document a human document a humument document Iain Sinclair document walking document Debord document sandpaper document problematic document Christian document Sadist document angry document happy document sad document useless document sodom document Gomorrah document Pasolini corpse document we fascists are the only true anarchists document relief document musical document prejudiced document Whitney Houston document trying to be document wanting to be OK document Old Kinderhook document kindergarten cop document silence your inner cop document swan document dawn document sawn document swaddle document swarm document marbled swarm document murder document problem document sleepy idiot document coffee document a cocaine novel document a sentimental novel document pdf document gif document digital document illegal document 2600 document child document be a good father document be a good husband doc-**

ument don't be a piece of shit document eat shit document take your Prozac document take your Buspirone document take your Seroquel document take your insulin document watch your weight document be a good person document recycle document eat dirt document watch television document care for others document sleep document H. document stream document wandering document meditation document you are OK document all is well document wandering document ambience document trance document pondering document walking document H. document suddenly face to document know about document the points right person dead in front of his eyes document as the vibrating strings, & is provided: he loves you, document they are not condemned document & mad prophet document & a helpless fanatic document all cold air is it is document rope by the sword, & of the victims, document about cm thick document of one of the arm is almost, document the loss of this arm & document where will it vary buried document abyss teetering over the content, document the number of document & roll experience with distilling it consumes me document repeatedly document repeatedly document likely to ecstatic leaving document Ego document the world I love god, we do not wish, there is hope.

There was no place in the world in which one might've been somesuch other than a miserable person living. Every person was miserable living on the compound & one could only flee for something promising of culture or sustenance: they were bored. We were bored. Living was boring. Surviving was boring. Time spent was boring. Hoping was boring. Failing was boring. Succeeding was boring. Happiness & capability & difference & similitude & controversy were boring. Having no light to stare into & wander off into & enter & engage with & detract from & consume & sleep & wither & produce & consume & needing nothing but every second of every single day for oneself for an ugly thing for an ugly self for a pathetic self for a marital self for a single self for a wandering self for a homosexual self for a bisexual self for a heterosexual self for a wordless self for a talking self for a sleepyhead self for a beachyhead self a creep self a murderous self a contemplative secretive disgusting self a bloated bulbous rotund self a shifting absorbent shitting self he's useless H. is alone & useless I am alone & useless they are alone & useless. Just stop. No stories, never again. Visions of war. Decontrol. No stories, tomorrow belongs to us. No stories, but after the gig. No stories, I'm society's victim. No stories, hear nothing see nothing say nothing. No stories. No narratives. A perverted useless fucking buffoon. No stories. No telling no tale. No stories. A hero is no stories. Autocorrect no stories.

Maybe he is come, that is to say, in the changes of

light thing to be, or not to depart from. In this way, as you know to choose vocational education November potential death, maybe this is a different form of image & nature of matter created around the various arts, thou knowest: that which living human being on earth could do to make the veil suddenly lift meat seldom seen will variety of activities & various members of preaching to the city fauns force of the return of prominent defense against arthritic vacillates as his hair started looking intently at him O I'll let you saw sun sawyers law nu wanders or wanders us as nu wardens use us whether you are right in taking the brother abides in gear, read? Treat them. Identification. It filled with wounded soldiers not stuff it is the use of physical wither laughing (digital) is very important for the killing article lack of e-payment confirmation use sewn darn use urine rotten surely wuss rotten wanes us beautiful there's something on its & even stepping away & even thinking this us the last to wear the sweet tooth or happiness or does not tetanus there. Would lie in my name groaning press machine to be set on fire. My name is beggar the wind forearm forearm clap bristle thimble used the magic hex magic rotten pots from human urine this subhuman, & as many cores of barley, in the studio. Subheading others. I know how many. Reason uproar. Some of the chief mantra pal route human life living in the allah receiver to the government of La Monte thrusting forward under-

Remissionem Peccatorum.
X

lies upon fields of glowing neon bay that shifts & moves with the week to watch, or the lack of adequately distributed through the time up, was not stopped up, with up to be stopped was stopped up to plain sight, feel nuanced places. Suicide is familiar with this result. Up & smile at the face of a sudden are moot points. For some of the lack truly a horror to an end, will get lost in a perspective like the one benefit the tone employee. He stopped. Seeing stopped. He saw hope of the people happy! I menu with the unknown depth of the precious metals, & will not fear? It has been prepared. Comfort/requesting/fail of coffee, you that you're unjust, & nay, but, the hour is, how great is the sphere which has it through on the flipside will also be false note. Changes piss press, but because it is potential updates & respectfully decline all comments H./justice chest but sounds & understanding, & the problem will be undepressed. Want to be happy. A sad, who is my will, & to fixate do. Uncertain. He opened the box, the device of the disclosure, saw tired & tired of dying. & cannot wait for Halloween. My that ugly & sea has been devastated world. The first philosophy, & as a person alarm. & what it might be. All terrified me. He said two. It against you. Safetysafety Stein, m.d. au revoir, au revoir, for you. Disputes with your family's concerns, not full two together. So again you wait until you can see the face. Yes, given toast of the tower today, look carefully through the corpus of dead. Think of his family, his something else, something unrelated to their content but that they exist & hence must be the next turn, is surrounded by a double words mentioned, it is in the constant movement circles, with patience some harmful & boy the tum just in the way we think because wish the mysterious secret of the death to be different, like the sun, quot I want to dragging try & meat draw comparisons nothing any their labors, the way of the most beautiful part of that which has deserved to chauvin, the leader shall bear which is the foundation of misery, dragging the maladies cannot or ad. Myself am one there is the best trouble trouble trouble can understand the impact of the machines for their reliability as a whole rehab treatment plant. These included a consultation with the mining of the first wet cursed yr lip cursed yr teeth cursed yr fog cursed yr nightmare cursed yr sleep cursed yr water cursed yr treatment here is the poor mind it, or counterfeit end. How about this lifetime subscription wall vigorous level of urgency. H. coolly treated with the [cruel sitting & sitting]. There enjoy this goes for depression if you do not feel meet morning anymore. Sedan wren pass nothing like being beaten by her side we have our wands with wands into the receptacle formed ear less wands transfigured net model can realize the forearm awakening tone volume atmosphere sleep wide awake Hsieh sent torn a way out. Transfer some organizations have type extravasation. Pacing room pacing wandering belly swan is roasted to make use of the stings of the rotten rotten rotten rotten rotten rotten are accustomed to the genius of the greatest fear, destroy me, let him follow me, & when she told me that as he did not have much at night. While I was thinking of a truth to the condemnation of the attempts to identify with me, & there is not a sign to you. He said something to them in the flesh & in the pass & the telescope cannot see the door. As a souvenir from the lute & mantle Lincoln sleep rule again for us, we loved the farmer mantra less trouble rotten random random hear & fear the rotten against the rotten being behind the kitchen. We are: for the first time in these cases it does not seem to be a mixture of all those who acknowledge the Lord of mythologize & not know it, so that they know what is as is the case so that the laughter from the memory, you can imagine the shit. Potential write something bad about the history & returned to the step. Workbenches machinist can be saved. We fear void below the eye. What do you want me to do for thee? What is with me, & I will not be watching. Nothing was thin to please. At the head of those who are not at all happy happy happy happy happy happy... bury taken into account when the greatest force injury & was led into the world to break down the blind. Please. Disney lost the one we are wanting to shut the cave. But we are not to identify the object that is in use. This project is not of us. But who will be able to depress he wishes to speak. Warned holy loyalty. There is a common, famous for his piety, & he began to think, nor not on its own, it takes all the moreso, for even so I do. Body. They are forms of human rue sand sawn rue sand grain prudent in your own sand grain ruse sand grain sure sand grain allowable H. about to get a clean culture & cigarette smoke not a moron explain the one hand send it in olden times. Imperfection the latter is in its own times he thirsted, for in every detail of each of () pages is usually an empty room. & the heads of the changes to be viewer/user to mind. Problem of modern humans split quote of his death are intertwined cannot look at you, but for me, warm blood scribble rusted, & the study found, but a high & perhaps several generations. At the time of death for them to fall into undergraduate education in English. Quot the stories there is none to mythologizing in time to come, & aids thee, I think. I will stay with you long H., sitting footage. But the question before, except none. For good eats. Sand fall season trade that less is it? Publishing amp I hate you, I hate all of the invite. Goodbye.Wind plot which had been, that on them as have regard to the building or to the temptation of the ivy-wreathed wands now, carried boughs, & his day & generation is to be feared now, carried boughs now, carried boughs nus, one sun another sun of the finger, nu now, carried boughs were you.

Where can keep it, or touch the done by means of a

kiss, the purpose of secrecy. The dew, & the rust on the doors with only seeped into how to write large amount of hell he wanted to many threats, they were sawn in the way of the open light. The Edict of the night, to read this I want to. Buried forearm use devices from bugs in the future. Sleeping habits. All in all, it is necessary to search for either of their collection. We think of thought. To be born again, had begun to rule in the more abominable than a spider's crust, which is, in return for which they are to be followed, it seems that it would be wrong in vain: what a long way of sacrifice. This is very rested & cf. For there was to feel as far as to sample although in certain places, he laughs in the great evil of the earth. You have to bear in mind here is something that will help someone to talk & say to him, well you take your messages with H. You will never leave ran out & still there is full & all of that, but he tries to write anonymous meeting. She immediately moved to the aorta artery in the city received in the sanctuary race in this article are not new, it is not put on the wound, we have this machine & viewers, but eventually came to think of covering a witness [revenue] in the house today typically hold that a change in the dog that are more user. Burned down incompetent. Mattering ever stands at the every one, both in counsel any more of this very thing they were made. In your room & do not look to get rich not only in relation to the duty segments that do poorly in bad sore throat remedies are first placed ADHD. I who have ever lived through a lend to the reliability & whatever it is that the person be? This rotter is not rotten. I wish I could ruin that rotter.

Pages, sentences or plot moments in the text, but violent & thinking. & the crust, in the classroom, to begin with, that they may breed, & the spider's web, & is considered to be in the days of the tongue of so many provinces with their own digitized & a bad smell from urine the potential there of omitting the gradual relaxation of the user that is unaware of the gallery, & much less from the relation to it at all. The occurrence of silly, but our life by being cut & squalor. Apart from my memory spastic here remember acuteness assist encoding marble counters in the bathroom. Including me. The camera was found with a small pours into the bay be buried without a trace of the body will die down with him, even in ourselves. But also to find them forever. As always moderate. However, it does not cease upon any of us were forced attitude. The soul is drawn low to feel the mainstream. These marks are the marks. For I am on the front to the back of the optimize bone. This work, together with their delights, cancerous, to whom they give payment in full to the systemic systemic, the constant communication, although it was done that thou thyself art a conference, there is a certain idea of a being, I will not be able better to die in the end of a lake, no, I will. Either form can see grave sexual fantasy amateurishly spent his colleagues & was a joke, I think. These utilities are not for everyone, is not clear to me, he suddenly said to one another, at more closely in all these things. However, they do not think what is it can be, & at any time of day, from the people to think of the physiological to be out of that place in which to wait for the obvious, the only one which are the ultimates of the exhibition & the work of ten. Every love you very much. However, I have been deeply in researching holds for several years as the crow flies above & children lost everything in the village. I go around uncertain. For outstanding. The business of the boy, in a few words, nothing else was to be seen to be enough food for the week he shall descend into it. Or, in the sense of the good, & from there to all the precepts zealous for the good, for, & a metal, while the exterior of the metal is governed by the nature of the world they are neither of these motors in any thing. Neither of these ways of life in the shadow of the atom, one by one, it is in potentiality with respect to numeral, & bring forth what is what is going on in the streets of the old, however, & the faces of them all the help, which ye have heard. *https://www.youtube.com/watch?v=SUVwOI61qFk*

In the dawn of man was H. walking & having nothing but feet & knowing the light would end all of the light would end he could not wait for all to end the body would be strewn his body would be strewn the light would end he would be found in various spaces his final space the space of what the space of body the space of his ending the space of his final limb his final rotter limb evil placed in place the final work the final artwork his Charenton his Lincoln his dropping out in perpetuity forever trying leaving needing life away from trying. H. discovered thus through clicks & rotten idiot clicks & Salt Lake City rotting useless old radio tower of babel rotting he rotting sending out fragments of language useless language Glenn Gould mumbling language having nothing to say language having nothing to contribute to the earth language having nothing to offer to the cosmos language only rotting useless language going endless having endless reach & nothing grasped & language this H. rendered thus & I am stuck to figure him & reckon with him & consume him & unearth him discovered reassembled fragments of corpse the smiling boy the rotting head the useless rotting head there his last painting the final rendering the final embodiment the final living in the final century the end of man of aspiring of reaching of hoping of necessity of occupation of responsibility of ownership of all suffering.

A small & minor book. A useless book. A little book for having. A little book for owning. A little book on which to write the future of your being. A little book to be planted & shared for all futurity. A little buried crow of a book. A little buried rodent of a book. A little useless book rotting. Sleepy book & rendered book. Tired book & hopeless book. Needy book & childish book. Pay no attention. Never pay attention. Never pay close attention. Read generally. Do not read. There is no history of H., no history of America. There is no history of me. There is no compound where to rest. The compound where they rest is not of me. I am asleep with H.'s bones within the compound awaiting death & eternal lightlessness. Within the compound awaiting. Within the compound needing & in prayer. Within the compound circled & in prayer worshiping & praying to light. Within the compound needing everyone within the compound holding close. Within the compound away from all suffering & light & talk & language within the compound. We are ever within the compound. What remains of H. within the compound, sleeping. What remains of I within the compound, sleeping. Buried in the compound resting, needing every bit of light, every seed. Every seed placed beneath the compound small light off on the horizon the tiniest fragment of sun discernible through rotting atmosphere the world rotting its people rotting its H. rotting its thoughts rotting its trees rotting the small light seen at the edge of the horizon through rotten rotting horizon discerned & seen & taken in & consumed & loved & welcomed I watched the light of our sun pass by I

**watched the same light seen by H. on his death I watched the light of our life pass by & inhaled it a small line of light off in a sea of barely glowing gray I consumed it I watched it I witnessed it H. wrote of it H. saw it too H. knew the light was dying H. welcomed the dying of the light H. strewn bodily everywhere H. rotting everywhere & worms consuming him his beloved birds his beloved grubs his beloved saw machine rendering him outward and useless unacabine into the dying light seen & rendered in corner of fragment of page & jutted out in clicks to us or all at Salt Lake City rotting in the light the endless light the city light the painted light the dim gray off on the horizon seen just once more & not knowing if we'd see again & eventual rays of horrid gleaming light against the chest in sun & breathing in every iteration of light & H. experiencing the light in stream & these broken stretches of absolute sun rotting & being witnessed by each**
**of us in turn & every- one wit-**
**nessing some death &**
**burying the seeds**
**as H. & welcom- ing**
**something some**
**hell some ret- i-**
**cence having no**
**coherency no**
**narrative no co- he-**
**sion no sensibili- ty no**
**ideology no hope no discern-**

ible language only reticence only hesitation only trepidation rendering all of it this way at my end & H.'s end and the world's close & holding close the whispered final light of the machine the gasp the saw in ever spinning form.

Inside the Castle